Introduction to Engineering Design

John E. Gibson
Oakland University

HOLT, RINEHART and WINSTON, INC.
New York, Chicago, San Francisco, Atlanta,
Dallas, Montreal, Toronto, London

Preface

One of the important goals of this text is motivation. One of the reasons that engineering is a popular career choice, I suspect, is that one can range from an honest, work-a-day, routine job to the highest levels of theory and creativity within its house. This broad spectrum has its disadvantages, however, since it makes definition of the term "engineering" more difficult. By introducing the philosophy of engineering very early in the curriculum we hope to aid in this understanding.

A purpose even more important than motivation is the introduction of the various technical areas of engineering to aid a student in his career choice. How is this to be done in a meaningful technical way given students with only a high school background? The solution attempted here involves the concept of the preliminary design process and requires macotechniques of engineering. These are suitable from a mathematical level and exciting from a conceptual level for the beginning engineering student. We deliberately avoid detailed analysis of elements. Rather, macroconcepts such as money, energy, time efficiency, and information are the symbols manipulated. Fortran, data reduction, and statistics are not uniquely related to preliminary design. However, we feel they are necessary tools for the young engineering student and unity is sacrificed in this cause.

All too often engineering students graduate with the idea that good engineering design is nothing more than a good technical design. An introduction to economics in engineering design at an early stage in engineering education accustoms the student to consider economic factors in all phases of engineering. This introduction can be reinforced in later courses if all laboratory reports and term projects must include a budget sheet.

One of the fundamental quantities dealt with by engineers is energy. Conservation of energy is readily grasped by students and energy balance provides a powerful analytical tool for the preliminary design process. The discussion of energy leads quite naturally into a discussion of the most common form of energy, namely heat energy, and the science of thermodynamics. The basic laws and their application in the study of engineering systems are presented. This is perhaps the most demanding of the macroconcepts covered in this book. Familiarization with a few of the basic concepts of thermodynamics encourages the student to approach his later course work more rationally. A similar argument can be made for probability and statistics.

It can be an interesting experience for a beginning engineering student to achieve the insight provided by information theory. Such basic concepts as signal-to-noise ratio, channel capacity, and redundancy provide a basis for intuitive understanding, not only of conventional communication systems but also of such diverse engineering systems as highway transportation networks. Although modern information theory is rather theoretical and abstract, there are these fundamental principles are easily grasped by the beginning engineering student.

In addition to overlooking economic factors, the beginning engineer is also quite apt to omit the human factors in engineering design. All too often machines are designed in a vacuum with little attention paid to the operator or to the interaction of the machine and humans. Focusing the attention of the freshman on such things as time-and-motion study, operator capability, and some of the sociological implications of large scale engineering systems helps him to be more aware of the relationship between his products and those for whom his products are intended.

What do we mean by calling certain topics "macroconcepts"? Why are these different from "microconcepts"? Quite obviously the term is subjective since it depends somewhat on the point of view. But, considering the position of an engineer in preliminary design, certain tools seem more basic than others. The preliminary designer is interested in answering questions for management, such as, How much will it cost?, What is its over-all operating efficiency? How long will it take? Does it defy any fundamental laws of information theory or thermodynamics? These macroconcepts are the sort of thing one needs for "back-of-the-envelope" calculations on new ideas. The typical scientist is wary of such simplifications and approximations but they are essential to the engineer.

Engineers are in wide agreement that materials are an important factor in engineering design. In fact, "materials" is one of the triumvirate of systems, energy, and materials, around which many modern schools build their programs. Yet there is no mention of materials in this course. Why not? Primarily because we have been unable to find a block of information that can be covered in one or two weeks and that can provide the student with useful design information. This question is worthy of further study.

When one considers the wide range of topics in this course and the short time allocated to each it seems difficult to avoid the objection that the covering is so thin as to be useless. We are concerned about this danger but it has apparently not been proven in practice. We see two reasons for this. First, the student finds the preliminary design philosophy to be a unifying element tying together the wide range of topics studied; second, the computation assignments are challenging engineering problems.

An important part of the course as it has been taught at Oakland University and Purdue is a weekly three-hour computation session. Here the student is a member of a small group, which tackles design problems of some complexity. During several of these computation periods the students obtain data on their own from various laboratory experiments. This serves as an introduction to advanced laboratory courses and provides realistic data reduction problems. In the first two computation sessions the student is introduced to Fortran and the digital computer. He then regularly uses the machine throughout the course.

Outside reading assignments on the history of engineering are assigned in a text which is chosen from among those mentioned in Chapter One. After the chapter assignments on the first day this text is not mentioned in class again. Ten percent of each hour examination is devoted to simple objective-type questions on the material. Lately we have supplemented this with "The Engineer" in the Time-Life series since this gives an excellent treatment of modern engineering.

On several occasions in which the author taught the course, the final five or six weeks of the computations were given over to a team design project. Each team reported on the results both in written form and at a formal oral presentation to outside judges. Experience indicates that the success or failure of such a project is critically dependent on the choice of topic. The key factors for success seem to be: (a) sufficient complexity to provide a variety of approaches; (b) technically simple enough to present few conceptual problems; (c) an economic flavor.

As our society becomes more and more technological it becomes increasingly important for all our citizens to be able to grapple with "the man-made world." Most students of the arts are required by their universities to acquire some familiarity with science. Presumably, this is not because they will practice such science, but because they should be aware of one or another aspect of physical reality to be called a whole man. There is some weight to the argument that physical laws are more effectively presented to such nonspecialists in the guise of the "man-made world" than by a detailed consideration of "nature." While a nonscientific citizen living in an urban environment can ignore much of the detailed content of the natural sciences, he cannot disassociate himself from technological reality while remaining an effectively functioning citizen. This argues for the acceptance of a first course in engineering as a possible vehicle for such understanding, provided such a course treats the subject liberally.

A freshman course then should serve a university function rather than a narrow professional function. In approaching the course described here we have tried to organize it so that it would be acceptable from this broad point of view. We were delighted recently to have the faculty at Oakland University accept this course into the university program as a satisfactory option in the science area. Students with majors in English, psychology, education, business, biology, and mathematics to name a few, have elected this course.

I am indebted to the Literary Executor of the late Sir Ronald A. Fisher, F.R.S., to Dr. Frank Yates, F.R.S., and to Oliver and Boyd Ltd., Edinburgh, for permission to extract Table 4.3 from their book *Statistical Tables for Biological, Agricultural and Medical Research.*

Thanks are also due to my collegues, especially D. E. Boddy and G. L. Wedekind.

John E. Gibson

Rochester, Michigan
March 1968

Contents

CHAPTER ONE

Introduction

1.1 WHAT IS ENGINEERING?

The title of this section is the sort of question everyone thinks he can answer, and the answer usually comes down to "engineering is what an engineer does." This kind of an answer certainly does not help us very much, but if we study the employment distribution of engineers this should give us some insight. In 1959 a large number of Purdue engineering graduates were polled to find out what kinds of jobs they held. Table 1.1 shows their job distribution at that time.

Table 1.1 contains some surprises. For example, by far the largest number of engineering graduates classify their jobs under human relations. Some young men choose engineering for a career because they like to deal with facts rather than with emotions and opinions, that

1

Table 1.1 Results of a Job Distribution Study of Purdue Engineering Graduates (in percent)[*]

Human Relations		42
Sales	12	
Technical management	23	
Nontechnical management	7	
New Developments		29
Design	13	
Development	11	
Research	5	
Operations		12
Construction	4	
Production	6	
Maintenance	2	
Preprofessional		5
Graduate study	1	
On-the-job training	1	
Military	3	
Miscellaneous		12
Engineering teaching	2	
Other engineering	4	
Other nonengineering	6	

[*] W. LeBold, *Purdue Univ., Eng. Bull.*, **44**, No. 1, 1960.

is, people. This is a perfectly valid reason, but obviously from these data we cannot assume that engineers do not deal with people. In fact, many successful engineers feel that "people problems" are the most difficult ones and the kind to which they devote much of their time.[1] Of course, most of the 42 percent who replied to the Purdue survey were probably concerned with technical sales and technical management, but this still means dealing with people and is not what we would call "engineering." We ask now, are the 58 percent remaining doing engineering? Those classified under preprofessional and miscellaneous (17 percent) can be eliminated. We seek now in the remaining 41 percent some function that is unique to engineering. Research may be vital to the rigor of the profession, but it is not unique to engineering. In

[1] Simply because 42 percent of the engineers in this study devote their time to human relations, we cannot say that each of these engineers devotes 42 percent of his time to this area. This invokes the ergodic hypothesis.

fact, it is difficult if not impossible to differentiate between engineering research and work done by other applied scientists. An applied mathematician, a physiologist, or a physicist may do research similar to the engineer, but this does not mean they are engineers. Likewise engineers may be very good at production, maintenance, and construction, but these are not uniquely engineering functions. Therefore, we can eliminate the classifications of operations and research as being special to engineering.

The design and development functions of engineering, however, are different (the remaining 24 percent). Here we see engineering in a pure state. In these functions the emphasis is not on *analysis*—that is, the breaking down into component parts—but rather on *synthesis*—that is, the assembling of pieces into a new functional whole. It is this emphasis on creativity, on the harnessing of nature to solve pressing problems of society, which differentiates an engineer from other scientists. The pure scientist asks questions of nature and values the answers for their own sake, not for their relevance to society. The engineer, on the other hand, applies the facts of nature to suit the needs and meet the goals of society. His profession has no meaning if separated from society's needs. It is the engineer's creative, factual approach to problems that makes him so valuable in other fields. Although Table 1.1 did not make the definition obvious, since fewer than one out of four practice "engineering," it did help us in our quest. Design and development can be considered to be design in the large sense, in that we synthesize or develop a solution to a problem and then supervise bringing the solution to a reality. This is what we mean when we say: *engineering is design.*

1.2   TRADITIONAL AND MODERN AREAS OF ENGINEERING

The engineer first appeared as a *master builder* and *military specialist.* He built the roads, fortifications, and the engines of siege needed for waging war. The *civil* engineer then appeared, practicing the same skills but for peaceful purposes. The nineteenth century and the harnessing of steam power during the Industrial Revolution required further specialization; the *mechanical* engineer was born. By the twentieth century further developments in technology required the skills of an *electrical* engineer and later the *chemical* engineer and the *aeronautical* engineer. Today there are at least fifty recognized engineering specialties. Almost all industries that employ engineers long enough (textile and ceramic engineering) or in a spectacular manner (nuclear and aerospace engineering) will find a specialty named for it. This is useful because it enables practitioners of the same specialty to communicate with each other through their own journals and to regulate their own professional conduct. At the same time, it may be confusing to the beginning student who does not have his particular interest represented by a separate department at his university.

The beginning student should not be overly concerned if the choices afforded him at his school do not seem to be keyed to today's opportunities. The facts are that all curricula contain the essentials to prepare you for an engineering career. A sound preparation will permit you to work in almost any field of engineering. This is especially important for the junior or beginning senior, for example, who suddenly decides that, although he is doing well in electronics, he is really interested in space-vehicle propulsion. The best move is not to switch departments and lose a year taking his degree in aerospace engineering, but to finish on time with good grades in electronics, then go to graduate school in aerospace engineering or take a job with an aerospace firm.

Fads occur in engineering education as they do in everything else. In the 1950s, electronics was the preferred field, then nuclear engineering, then aerospace engineering, and now systems engineering seems to be coming to the fore, followed closely by biological engineering. All these are interesting and exciting areas in which to work, and a beginner certainly can aim for whatever field interests him. He should choose the department within his school that seems most closely attuned to his aims. However, his initial choice does not forever bar him from changing his mind or, in most cases, even impede his progress if he switches to another area.

1.3   THE MISSION OF MODERN ENGINEERING

Engineers should serve the needs of society. Engineering should be responsive, for example, to problems such as those brought on by the growth of the megalopolis that in 30 years will stretch from Milwaukee and Chicago in the west, through Detroit and Toledo, to Cleveland and Pittsburg in the east. As the population of this area becomes more dense, and it will double in the next 30 years, the impact of technology will continue to increase accordingly. Water pollution, the ecology of the Great Lakes area, mass surface transportation, more efficient means of energy conversion, application of exotic materials developed in the space program—all of these are area problems. Each part of our country and of the world yields its own list of problems to be solved. There are also worldwide challenges to be met by the engineer, such as the development of marine areas, the conservation of natural fuel resources, and the application of engineering methods to medicine and the life sciences.

More and more often, political decisions at the highest levels of government hinge on the technological aspects of the problem. Thus engineers must learn to cooperate with their fellow citizens and legislators in determining the overall impact of proposed solutions. The challenge of the space age will face engineers for the foreseeable future. The design of efficient energy units, closed-cycle life-support systems, and materials and systems that are capable of operation without maintenance for years in a hard vacuum under intense radiation and extreme temperature ranges are obvious examples of technical challenges.

The impact of the digital computer on engineering is so great that it requires special consideration.

Here is a list of specific things the digital computer does very well and which have had an impact on engineering design.

> a. The power of the computer to make arithmetic manipulations: A modern computer takes only a few ten thousandths of a second to multiply or divide two numbers. Addition and subtraction are done even faster. Thus the engineer can use the computer to make long and complex calculations very quickly and without fear of mistakes. Therefore, detailed and precise calculations which previously might have been prohibitively expensive become economical. Rough approximations and simplifications which might yield erroneous or inaccurate results can be replaced by more precise approaches that might have been impossible to complete by hand.
>
> b. The computer can store and recover almost instantly long lists of tabular data. The engineer can thus use first-hand experimental data in his design work rather than approximations.
>
> c. The computer can be made to repeat calculations for slight variations of design parameters by adding only a few instructions.

Thus, the engineer can calculate many solutions for his design rather than assume that the solution is well behaved between widely scattered check points as he might be forced to if his calculations were made by hand. Furthermore, the computer can be made to search for optimum configurations. We discuss this further in Chapter 10.

d.   The computer can store programs. Thus, the engineer need never begin from the beginning on a design he has done previously. He can also use other engineers' programs in his design thus further multiplying his effectiveness.

e.   The computer can be used to simulate, that is dynamically model, real systems such as aircraft and oil refineries which are much too complex and expensive for the engineer to use in his experimentation.

f.   The computer can transmit and receive data from remote terminals and other computers, thus further enhancing its usefulness.

g.   Because of its speed and data handling capacity the computer can be programed to consider a wider range of design possibilities than an engineer could by himself, thus extending the generality of his design.

h.   The computer can be used to present data visually as on a television screen to help the engineer appreciate the overall appearance of his design.

i.   The computer can be programed to proceed directly from the engineer's design to the automatic control of the machine tools which turn the design into physical reality.

j.   All of these advantages can be made available to engineering students as well as to engineers in practice. Thus not only is the practice of engineering advanced but engineering education can make a great leap forward into practical reality.

k.   The engineering of computers and computer systems will themselves be increasingly important areas of employment for engineers in the future.

A student just beginning his professional training usually does not consider the role that engineering plays in society. The student may say that he has all he can do merely to keep up with his class assignments. In a way this is true, but in another it is not. We are all too busy to take time to consider the larger questions, and the older one grows the busier he gets. Vice-Admiral H. G. Rickover, in an eloquent speech before the British Association for the Advancement of Science in 1965, pointed out that although engineering stands on the threshold of the liberal professions, it has not as yet stepped across. He points out,

> It has as its theoretical foundation a body of systematic knowledge, an academic discipline as rigorous and extensive as that of other learned professions. It has a highly developed technique for applying this specialized knowledge to practical problems. But today there is no absolute requirement that an engineer must be a liberally educated man, nor has engineering adopted the kind of ethical code that governs the older professions of medicine and law.

For the good of society the engineer must earn the right to have the integrity of his professional judgment upheld. The technologist who bows to immediate pressures fails in his professional duty. Rickover cites case after case in which the technological facts are ignored by special interest groups intent on immediate gains. He mentions the commercial deep-sea-fishing fleets of Norway, Russia, and Japan that are destroying the very whales on which their continued livelihood depends; the production of biologically "hard" detergents for profit while the pollution of our streams increases; the opposition of pharmaceutical interests to drug regulation while thalidomide babies are born; and the improper use of pesticides and weed killers that poison soil, rivers, and wild life. Rickover takes a dim view of the future of democratic society unless what he calls a "humanistic technology" prevails. The need is for a technology that is enlightened to its responsibility and firm in its resistance to improper use of its advancements.

1.4   THE PURPOSE OF THIS BOOK

We take as a starting point that the essence of engineering is design. Thus, in order to learn engineering, it seems we should concentrate on design. Twenty-five or thirty years ago this is exactly what was done in all engineering schools. The mechanical engineering student methodically designed a steam turbine, the young electrical engineer designed an electric transformer, and the aspiring civil engineer designed a bridge. Unfortunately, the design rules were empiric, and so much time was spent doing routine computations by hand that little time was left for understanding the problem in depth. This sort of brain-numbing labor was uninviting and, as events proved, not suitable for preparing men to solve the new problems of the electronic age, the nuclear age, and the space age. Design is still in many cases a repetitive process, but this iteration is now swiftly performed by computers, thus freeing the engineer for creative tasks.

The approach to design that is taken in this text is similar to the process of *preliminary engineering* or the *systems approach* or even *operations research* in the sense that when we consider a problem presented by society, we will also consider its political, sociological, and economic aspects, as well as its technological overtones. This approach to design requires the use of a number of "macrotechniques" such as energy flow, information theory, and thermodynamics, as well as tools such as statistics, economic calculations, and data handling.

In a sense this text is the first step in an iterative process of education. Assuming that the student has had little or no college-level material previously presented to him, we will introduce the philosophy of engineering. You will see how an engineer goes about identifying and solving an engineering problem, what tools he needs, and what his methods are. At almost every step along the way we will make assumptions or approximations or use physical laws (or microtechniques) that you should not be able to accept. You should not accept them on authority, since this is contrary to the basic concept of science, and you should certainly not accept them without understanding them. What you should do is "play the game under protest." Say to yourself, "*If* this law of thermodynamics is really true and *if* this chemistry is correct, *then* I will work with the result pending further investigation." This approach to design should show you how the more advanced and detailed courses in your curriculum fit together to derive and develop the laws that we will be introducing here for the first time. Thus, you will approach these more advanced courses with a better idea of why they are being taught, and you will get more out of them. This is the second step in the iteration procedure. Later steps will follow in your senior electives and industrial experience or graduate school.

1.5 A COMMENT ON REPORTING PROCEDURES

In Chapter 2 we begin our study of the methods of gathering, manipulating, and presenting engineering data. Here and throughout our work we will take what may seem to you unnecessary pains to set up a number of apparently unnecessary rules. For example, we will insist that your homework be done in a specific form. We will insist that computations and graphs be done in a certain way. We will even require you to form your numerals in a prescribed fashion. Although the well-motivated student will accept these disciplinary matters with good grace, perhaps a word of explanation on why they are considered necessary would not be out of place.

The examples and problem assignments in this book have been chosen to display the point at issue while remaining as simple to compute as possible. Sometimes it is possible to see through such simple examples to the answer without using the suggested method. If you are tempted to do this, remember that the method is really the whole point of the exercise. So if you miss the method, you miss the point.

Directions on the form for preparing written reports are important for somewhat different reasons. The object of preparing a written report on a subject is to save the reader's time. Generally speaking, the time of the man you report to is worth more than yours. He may have as many as twelve men whose work he must guide and understand.[2] He could probably do the work he has assigned you more accurately and more quickly than you can, but he has others to supervise and counts on you to do the job properly and to inform him of the results in a standard way so he can digest them quickly. This means that you should reverse the natural-appearing, step-by-step, chronological procedure that you used to get your answer. That material must be included, in an appendix perhaps, but it will be examined only if you deliver an unexpected result. Your group leader will want to see the results first, then the explanations. In a laboratory report most engineering supervisors turn directly to the graph showing the results of the experiment. This is why everything of importance must be included on this one sheet. An engineering professor of my acquaintance has a dramatic way of emphasizing this point. As the report of the results of the first experiment in his course is handed to him by the student, he immediately turns to the graph, tears it out of the report, and hands all the other material back to the surprised student. The grade is based solely on the graph. A forgotten name, date, or experiment title weighs heavily. Usually one dose of this rather strong medicine effects a cure.

In homework assignments neatness and form are important for several

[2] Management studies seem to indicate that twelve is an upper limit for direct, day-by-day supervision. If a group grows beyond this level it should be divided.

reasons. First, we find that many simple arithmetic mistakes are due to lack of order in intermediate calculations. You are liable to misread carelessly formed numbers or add numbers from the wrong column and so forth. In the pressure of examinations small bits of scrap work contribute errors.

Many research laboratories have a rule that no loose paper may be used and no erasures are allowed. All work must be entered neatly in a bound laboratory book. This procedure began because of patent regulations but has been widely adopted because it reduces careless errors and later difficulty in deciphering the meaning of your work.

Another reason for neatness is that it makes a good impression on your readers. Another is that it helps the grader discover and correct the source of any mistakes.

1.6   GOOD READING HABITS

Here, let us illustrate the difference between reading for knowledge and reading for pleasure. The technical writer avoids synonyms, analogies, indirection, and many other common literary techniques. He must call a spade a spade and keep on calling it a spade every time he sees it. It is no crime to use the same noun a dozen or more times on a single page. The reader is not bored, because he seeks detailed information, not simply an impression. One reads more slowly and carefully when reading technical material. One develops a careful sense of detachment and noncommitment. The reader says to the author, "I don't believe you; neither do I disbelieve you. I refuse to commit myself until you prove what you say." This attitude is very difficult to sustain, but it is essential.

One carefully searches for the expressed and implied assumptions of an author's work. This is difficult because, especially in introductory textbooks, the author often finds it difficult to make clear the limitations of the theory he is discussing within a reasonable space.

In the chapters that follow we list the pertinent technical references for this text. In addition, Appendix A contains a book list for engineers. This list was compiled by the student members of the Purdue chapter of Tau Beta Pi, the national engineering honor society. Finally, before leaving the subject of reading, we wish to give a few pointers on general professional reading for future engineers.

There are a number of historical accounts of engineering technology available in almost any library. Two particularly handy ones are *The Story of Engineering* by James Kip Finch[3] in paperback and R. S. Kirby and others, *Engineering in History*.[4] Reading history gives one perspective and a sense of continuity. Another area that should be of interest is the biographies and the collected works of great engineers. The careful reader will find much to reward him in such a study.

The area of general science is likewise very fruitful. The young engineer should graduate from popular mechanics and hot-rod magazines to *Scientific American* and the IEEE *Spectrum*. These are authoritative journals with semipopular accounts of the latest scientific developments written by professional scientists. Since most engineers will be employed by industry after graduation, it would be wise to become aware of the economic facts of life. For a well-illustrated and well-written account of modern industry, the student should read *Fortune* each month. After reading several issues, you should be quite aware that all companies are *not* alike and that there is much more to consider during an employment interview than what the starting salary is and where the firm is located. Since *Fortune* is a monthly, it concentrates on general overview articles, which are probably just what you want. For a closer, detailed view, read weeklies such as *Forbes* or *Business Week*. Weekly news magazines such as *Time, Newsweek, U.S. News & World Report* are also valuable. Even if you follow all of these suggestions in an attempt to set up a well-balanced reading program, it should not take more than 7 or 8 hours a week. A skillful reader reads at the rate of about a minute per book page. If you cannot read at least one half this rate, you are a slow reader. Reading well is an important skill that should be acquired as soon as possible. If you are not a good reader, your progress in college and in the business world will be hindered. Lose no time signing up for a speed-reading course to correct this deficiency.

[3] J. K. Finch, *The Story of Engineering* (Garden City, N.Y.: Anchor Books, Doubleday and Co., Inc., 1960).
[4] R. S. Kirby, S. Withington, A. B. Darling, and F. G. Kilgour, *Engineering in History* (New York: McGraw-Hill, Inc., 1956).

CHAPTER TWO

The Preliminary Design Process

2.1 INTRODUCTION

The procedure an engineer goes through in surveying a new technical task in order to lay out the broad outlines of the problem and its proposed solution is often called *preliminary design*. In companies that work with government agencies, preliminary design consists of responding to requests for quotations sent out by the government or in submitting unsolicited proposals on new technical developments in which a company thinks the government might be interested.

In more conventional industrial situations, the preliminary design group functions within the corporation. Figure 2.1 shows an organization

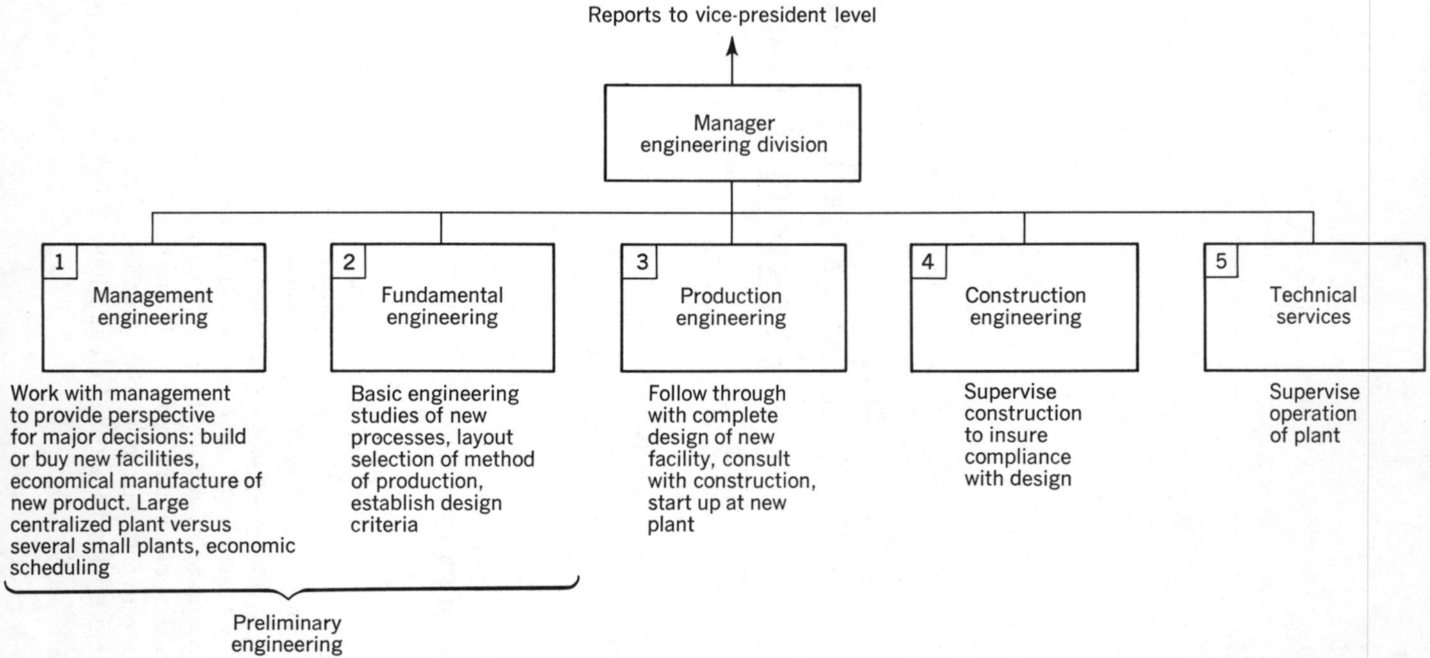

Figure 2.1. An organization chart for a large, successful company dealing in consumer products.

14

Reports to vice-president level

Manager engineering division

1 Management engineering

Work with management to provide perspective for major decisions: build or buy new facilities, economical manufacture of new product. Large centralized plant versus several small plants, economic scheduling

2 Fundamental engineering

Basic engineering studies of new processes, layout selection of method of production, establish design criteria

3 Production engineering

Follow through with complete design of new facility, consult with construction, start up at new plant

4 Construction engineering

Supervise construction to insure compliance with design

5 Technical services

Supervise operation of plant

Preliminary engineering

chart for a very large and successful consumer products corporation that spends $20 million to $30 million each year on new process development. The branches under the engineering manager are organized essentially in accordance with the chronology of the design of a new facility. Boxes 1 and 2 are what we call preliminary design.[1]

Management is charged with the responsibility of directing the operation and growth of the company in an organized fashion. Management invests in research and development and runs market surveys to generate ideas for new products. In effect, it attempts to find out what the consumer likes about its own and its competitors' products in a certain field and develops ideas for more satisfactory new products. This is a very difficult procedure, and sometimes a company confuses what the consumer should want and what the consumer really does want. The Ford Motor Company's "Edsel" is an example of the former, and the "Mustang" is an example of the latter.

Creativity in the development of new ideas is certainly desirable, and a person with the gift for developing new concepts to meet a given need will always be in demand. Preliminary design, however, should not be confused with "imagineering," inventing to order, creativity, "brain storming," or the like. Preliminary design is a very definite and objective scientific procedure that is enhanced by creativity but not dependent on it.

Let us consider the way the consumer products company shown in Figure 2.1 goes about preliminary design. The group represented by Box 1 conducts feasibility studies that provide management with (a) the estimated cost of developing a new process and (b) the time needed to bring the new plant on stream. Management provides market studies and checks the legal aspects of the problem. The decision of whether to proceed with the fundamental engineering is then made. One out of three of the projects for which full-scale feasibility studies are made in Box 1 is accepted and forwarded to the group represented by Box 2.

In addition to comparing various methods of producing the new product, fundamental engineering considers locations for the new plant and the time order of construction if several plants or processes are to be constructed; it establishes general specifications on unit processes, and makes detailed cost studies for capital funding requirements. In comparison

---

[1] For another view of the design process see E. V. Krick, *An Introduction to Engineering and Engineering Design* (New York: John Wiley and Sons, Inc., 1956), Chapt. 6.

with the later stages, the cost of developing a proposal through the processes in Boxes 1 and 2 is negligible. At this point, however, a binary (yes/no) decision on whether to proceed is needed.

The cost of production engineering is several orders of magnitude greater than the cost of preliminary studies, and the cost of construction and marketing is even several orders of magnitude greater than that. Preliminary engineering is thus a very sensitive area. A decision that costs $100 to make in Box 1 can influence expenditures of up to $1 million in Box 4. In terms of information theory, we would say the gain is 10,000 to 1, and therefore the decision is critical. To initiate a serious preliminary design study, someone in authority must generate enthusiasm on the basis of a fragmentary research result or a small preliminary market survey. This initial uninformed enthusiasm, however, must not be allowed to push an idea past Box 2 because beyond this point large sums of money have to be committed. On the other hand, the fact that only two out of three projects are rejected in Box 1 probably reflects a very conservative management policy in the company under study. More studies and a higher rejection rate might mean more money-making ideas. In the illustrative company, over 90 percent of those ideas studied in Box 2 eventually go into production. This number is perhaps too high and may indicate a restriction by management on those ideas fed into Box 1. An open and easy acceptance of the new ideas being fed into Box 1 coupled with a very cold and careful examination of those plans coming out of Box 2 would seem to be required of management.

Once the decision to proceed past Box 2 has been made, all possible speed must be employed to complete the design and construction and to market the product. No changes in goals or methods should be allowed. This may seem like harsh doctrine but the reasons for it are several:

> 1. If the idea of interfering with detailed design becomes current, hasty decisions will be made at the preliminary stage by arguing, "Well, I'm not positive about this point, but let's give it a month and see how it looks then."
> 2. Once a product has been approved for production, all possible speed may be necessary to maintain a competitive advantage. Design copying and loss of exclusive markets may be the result of time lost in production design and construction.
> 3. Because of the cost of production design and construction,

a change at this stage becomes exceedingly costly and, when coupled with the time lost, may change the whole return-on-investment picture.

4. The chance for error is magnified if several modification for a system are circulating in the company. Inevitably as more and more people are brought into the production design and construction phases, it becomes more and more difficult to control and supervise each person's work. Often the result of introducing changes is not the improvement one hoped for but an increase in errors and general confusion.

5. A team of people can be inspired to strive for a goal by determined leadership. However, if the team gets the idea that a full-speed-ahead command may soon be followed by a stop-all-engines-and-change-course command, it is unlikely to put out maximum effort. Thus, frequent changes of design goals may cut the efficiency of the team. In addition, an outside vendor cannot be held to a firm delivery date if he is directed to make changes after the contract is signed. Oftentimes a vendor will make a small design change the excuse for slowing down his phase of the whole operation to a more comfortable pace, upsetting the entire schedule.

It might be interesting to compare the principles under which the particular consumer products corporation discussed above operates with the way the Department of Defense (DOD) organizes its research and development. The DOD defines six steps in the research and development (R & D) function.

1. *Research* is concerned with the investigation of natural physical phenomena. It is goal directed only in the most general sense.

2. *Exploratory development* is the solution of specific military problems stopping short of major development projects. It includes fundamental applied research on laboratory models of hardware. It is pointed toward specific military problem areas with a view toward developing and evaluating the feasibility of proposed solutions.

3. *Advanced development* includes all projects that have moved into the development of hardware for experimental or operational testing. Included, for example, are projects so large that they

are individually identified in the DOD budget (so-called "line items"), such as VTOL aircraft, the X-15 aircraft, hydrofoil boats, and so on.

4. *Engineering development* is the development of items designed for field service use but not yet approved for procurement.

5. *Management and support* includes the installation and operation of test ranges, laboratories, test aircraft, and the like.

6. *Operational system development* is the management of systems approved for production and service use.

The concept of preliminary design developed in this text centers on the initial definition and development of a goal-oriented project. Thus research as defined by the DOD is outside the scope of preliminary design. Item (2), exploratory development, covers the scope of design but with one major omission; it starts after the problem has been defined. We will find that properly defining the problem is more than half the battle. Thus, a problem definition phase must be added to the DOD concept of exploratory development before it would be equivalent to preliminary design. Since item (2) goes on to cover a laboratory-model hardware phase and an evaluation phase, it satisfies our definition of preliminary design, provided that this definition phase is added.

Items (3) through (6) on the DOD list represent successive iterations in the design process.

We have chosen preliminary design as a vehicle for this first course in engineering for several reasons:

1. It matches the interests of beginning students who are taking a first look at engineering and who would like to know what engineering is about.

2. At least in broad outline, many of the concepts of preliminary design are capable of being grasped without advanced mathematics.

3. It provides motivation for taking further courses by showing the need for the detailed technical knowledge that is provided in the following years.

4. It helps a student choose his major area of specialization by illustrating what various types of engineers do on the job.

In the following sections we will discuss the iterative nature of the design process and several of the tools needed to make design decisions.

2.2 DESIGN IS AN ITERATIVE PROCESS

Iteration means to repeat or to go over again. We must go over or repeat the design process because the first time through we cannot make firm decisions since the data needed will be the result of the design process itself. This may sound complicated, but Figure 2.2 helps to clarify the process.

Let us apply this procedure to the consumer products firm described above and diagramed in Figure 2.1. The *start* is usually the desire to show a profit for the year. Management recognizes a new market or need. Suppose, to give a concrete example, our company manufactures household cleaners. Management *recognizes* that a new all-purpose liquid cleaner containing kerosene has been introduced by a small company on the East Coast. By immediate *comparison,* management sees that it does not have a similar product, and it decides to *evaluate* the competitor's product. A quick check of the regional sales office shows excellent market penetration in the limited area in which the competitor's product is now being offered. Management decides to check more carefully, that is, to *iterate*. The process can be quite informal at this point. Perhaps it merely means that the sales manager calls the regional sales office for more information after he reads the regular weekly report. He in turn suggests management should follow this up.

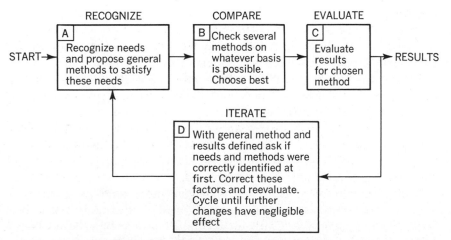

Figure 2.2. Design as an iterative process.

The second cycle starts when management *recognizes* that more information is needed. *Comparison* reveals that our company considered such a product several years ago but decided not to proceed because the product was hard on hands and because housewives appeared not to like the smell of kerosene in their liquid cleaner. However, *evaluation* of a market survey of users of the new product reveals rather general acceptance. The pine-oil scent covers the kerosene smell, and women like the product's grease-cutting power. Sales appear to be increasing, and an imaginative television advertising program has begun. The report to management concludes that although the product is based on a gimmick and management's original decision was probably correct on a long-term basis, the competitor's product could develop into a major competitor in the next few years if it were to be aggressively pushed. Management decides to look more carefully into this competition.

The third cycle starts by management feeding the group represented by Box 1 in Figure 2.2 the ground rules for a decision. "Provide the information and perspective for the following major policy decision: Should we develop a product that will compete point for point with the competition while at the same time overcoming its drawbacks? Thus we need the data to decide on the fourth cycle: Should management send the new product into fundamental engineering?"

The more technical aspects of preliminary design also follow this same iterative procedure. Suppose the result of the fourth iteration is to send the new product to fundamental engineering. The team in Box 2 will *recognize* various general methods of producing the product. They will *compare* these general methods and *evaluate* the best. They will then prepare to make a more detailed consideration of costs and techniques involved in the chosen method, again by an iterative process. In the following chapters we will consider some of the tools used in this process.

Before we close this section, a few more words on the way management forms the questions it puts to the investigating team are in order. This is the most sensitive of all parts of the process. A badly formed question results in an improper answer, and perhaps neither party will realize this fact until it is too late. There will be no self-check in the process. Management *thinks* it has asked the right question, and the investigating team *thinks* it has responded.

Notice that in the third cycle management worded its question in such a way as to also explain why it wanted the information. If it had said something like "Can we develop a kerosene-base liquid household cleaner?" the answer would have been, "Yes." But this is not what management needs to know. The technical problem should not be divorced from questions of timing, marketing, long-term corporate strategy, and economics. In terms of *game theory*, business is a competitive game in which the moves and countermoves of your opponents (competitors) are an important element of your success or failure. Thus, if the investigating team knows the reason for the question, it can make a more intelligent evaluation.

2.3   THE BASIC TOOLS OF DESIGN

The basic tools in preliminary engineering design are few in number. The importance of each tool varies from task to task. Sometimes only one or two of these tools are needed. This fact is illustrated by the examples we consider in each chapter. Granted they are simple examples, but they are meaningful. Engineers engaged in a given specialty will use certain of these methods more often than others, but all the basic ideas come into work sooner or later.

A young man interested in a career in civil engineering might argue that he can see the need for learning about economics, the strength of materials, the principles of statics, and the use of computers, but learning about human factors, the dynamics of oscillating systems, and information theory might appear useless to our aspiring civil engineer. The notorious experience with the Tacoma Narrows Bridge a few years ago, which went into vertical oscillation under the force of a strong steady horizontal wind and finally broke up, illustrates the need for dynamic studies of supposedly static structures. Human factor studies include the study of human reaction time to sudden stimuli. Ignorance of such data in the past has led highway designers (civil engineers) to place turnoff signs too close to the exits on turnpikes. The result has been traffic tie-ups and many preventable accidents near these exists, as motorists suddenly attempt to change lanes while approaching their exit. The use of information theory and the concepts of channel capacity have led to a reorganization of traffic flow in the Holland Tunnel in New York, with a substantial increase in flow as a result. We discuss this point in Chapter 9. The moral is: No one can neglect any of the basic tools of engineering design. The following is a discussion of these tools or macroconcepts.

Economics

Economic concepts are essential throughout the design process. The original impetus to initiate design studies is almost always economic. But even when the profit motive is removed, economic characteristics are often used to help decide between two possible methods of approach. When he is asked to make a feasibility study of a new proposal it is expected that the engineer will include cost estimates in his report. It is also expected that an engineer will understand the concepts of fixed costs and operating costs, and how to choose the optimum operating point for the scheme he is designing.

Energy

The economical use of energy and other natural resources have long been a basic concern of the engineer. Since energy costs money, the engineer is determined to apply it efficiently. Quite often efficiency calculations are best made by considering the rate at which energy is being used, that is, power. By calculating the overall energy requirements for a process, the engineer can often find the economic costs and will thus be able to estimate the profit. This estimate permits management to decide to advance to the next step of detailed design or to seek other approaches. The efficiency calculation is also quite useful in comparing several components that are designed for the same service.

Thermodynamics

Perhaps the most common form of energy is heat energy, and the engineer must often take it into consideration in preliminary design. The concepts, indeed the very words, of thermodynamics are strange to our ears; yet they are based on three quite simple observational (experimental) facts. Because the theory of thermodynamics, which has been built up bit by bit through the years, agrees so well with experimental evidence and has been so useful in helping us to discover new facts, it is one of the most important of the engineering sciences.

Information Concepts

Unlike energy, which has always been the concern of the engineer, information concepts have been considered important for engineers only in the past 20 years. Telephone engineers have long studied information theory in their attempts to push as much information through a telephone line as possible. Only recently, however, have we begun to realize that the concepts of information rate, signal-to-noise ratio, entropy and channel capacity, and so on have a very general validity. The young engineer beginning his training today will doubtless witness an even wider use of these ideas in the years ahead. The reason for including information concepts in this text is their importance in preliminary design. They establish the ultimate limits on the operation of a wide variety of engineering devices.

Human Factors

The engineer must never forget that whatever he designs is meant to be used by human beings. The concern here is not with attractiveness or sales appeal. We mean that unless the designer goes to apparently absurd lengths to prevent it, people will operate the device incorrectly. Contrary to the designer's claims when this happens, it is not because people are stupid. Rather, if this word is to be used at all it applies to the designer. Usually when a device is not properly operated, it indicates that the designer has exhibited another common human attribute, namely, egocentricity. The designer who makes a design decision so the implementation will be easy for himself rather than for the user is egocentric because he is concerned with his own problems rather than those of the user.

Examples of such designs are common in everyday life. For example, the parking brake of many automobiles more than 6 months old is inoperative. Obviously the brake should be so designed that it is impossible to drive the car while the brake is set. Such a design would be quite simple. The fact that it has not been done is because automobile designers insist on saying, "Well, people ought to know enough to release the parking brake before driving."

The airplane cockpit is a notorious example of extremely poor judgment in human factors. And here the penalty for an error is not simply a burned-out brake lining. This has come about because of the gradual addition of flight instruments, as airplanes have become more complex, and reluctance on the part of the aircraft industry to adopt integrated displays.

Optimization Theory

The theory of parameter optimization has become important to the engineer ever since the advent of the digital computer. It is now possible to automate the repetitive or iterative features of design, which results in the elimination of the drugdery of design while at the same time speeding up the process and yielding better results. We will consider this important new approach to design below.

2.4   AN EXAMPLE IN PRELIMINARY DESIGN

In this section we will briefly consider an example in preliminary design. We will attempt to illustrate how one begins the process of design and how the process isolates key factors for consideration in the next design cycle.

Industrialized societies, such as exist in many parts of the world today, use enormous quantities of fresh water. Even though with proper management the total fresh water supply of the globe seems adequate for the foreseeable future, this does not insure that adequate supplies will always be available when and where people need them. Locally deprived areas such as arid portions of the Middle East and the Los Angeles Basin in the United States already present a real problem. One proposed solution is the distillation of huge quantities of sea water.

Saline water conversion is still relatively expensive and obviously is not the way to cure such difficulties as those New York City recently experienced because of the lack of observing even the basic principles of conservation. Another similar example is the eastern Great Lakes region, where lack of control of industrial pollution and proper sewage treatment facilities is rapidly turning Lake Erie into a large open cesspool.[2]

In 1952, the Office of Saline Water was created within the Department of the Interior of the U.S. Government to study the problem of saline water conversion. This office has supervised research and constructed pilot plants of various kinds. Its present goal is to learn how to produce large quantities of potable water from saline or brackish water at a total cost of less than 60 cents per 1000 gallons. The present cost is about $1.25 per 1000 gallons.

[2] B. Commoner, *Science and Survival* (New York: The Viking Press, 1966), p. 12.

Suppose you were asked to make a preliminary study of saline water conversion for a specific situation. For instance, you might be asked to investigate what kind of system will produce a given flow per day at the least total cost. A number of processes have been proposed. Some are presently proved in practice; others, of theoretically higher efficiency, depend on one or more unproven concepts. Thus you must choose between the tried and true and the experimental. Data are available from the Office of Saline Water, from several books, and from many articles in engineering journals.[3]

This problem has a number of desirable features as a design exercise. It is topical; it has social impact; research data are available from a wide variety of sources; economics are important in the solution; and a judgment must be made on the risk of incorporating new research results into the design.

We assume that your design team has never even heard of the problem before. It's a priori knowledge is zero. Step one is to get all available literature from the library. (Now you wish you were a speed reader.) A few popular articles will give you an overall picture, but these will be quickly discarded for more factual material. Step two is the identification of the various proposed methods of conversion. Step three is to evaluate each method and to either reject it or place it aside for further study. The criteria for this judgment are (*a*) the technical suitability of the method, (*b*) its cost, and (*c*) the time scale involved in the project. Step four is a further careful study of those methods that survived the first screening. Can you identify these steps with one of the boxes in Figure 2.2?

Probably there will be included in this group both old and new methods. Now the agonizing decision must be made to designate one method as first choice and another as second choice. Detailed reasons for the choices should be given. The criteria used in making the evaluation must be stated. The reason for giving a second choice is to minimize delay in reorganizing should the first choice fail to meet the objectives.

The reason the decision in step four is called "agonizing" is that you will feel rushed, that your knowledge is inadequate, and that you would like to ask for more time to get more information, but the additional time will not be given. You will wish you had worked harder, earlier, and overtime to meet the deadline.

[3] For an introduction to the topic see G. D. Friedlander, "Science and the Salty Sea," *IEEE Spectrum*, **2**, No. 8, August 1965, pp. 53–64.

2.5   PROJECT PLANNING AND SCHEDULING: PERT AND CPM

Many research and development projects in the past decade have become so large and involved that it is impossible for any one person to be aware of how the project is proceeding. Many millions of dollars, hundreds of thousands of men and 2 or 3 years of time may be involved.[4] Often the project is for a device or system unlike anything previously attempted, and therefore past experience is no guide. The SNARK and NAVAHO air-breathing guided missiles are examples of well-conceived projects in the early 1950s that were less than totally effective because their completion took longer than originally planned. In the development of the ATLAS and the TITAN, two ballistic missiles of the same generation, considerable costly duplication seems to have occurred because of the lack of planning. In an attempt to bring order into the planning of such complex programs, a management method called PERT (Program Evaluation and Review Technique) was developed in 1959 by the Department of Defense. A similar method called CPM (Critical Path Method) was developed almost simultaneously by industry.[5] In PERT the primary emphasis is on the time of completion of each work segment whereas in CPM cost is also a factor. These techniques are based on the mathematics of linear programing but can be explained without going into mathematical detail.

Consider the everyday practice of preparing breakfast. Here are the steps involved:

1.   Mix frozen orange juice and pour into glasses; 3 minutes required.
2.   Fry bacon; 12 minutes.
3.   Scramble eggs; 4 minutes.
4.   Make toast; 4 minutes.
5.   Set table; 6 minutes.

---

[4] The NASA moon program, for example, is funded at approximately $6 billion per year or almost 1 percent of the gross national product. It alone could absorb every new Ph.D. in the physical sciences and engineering in the United States.

[5] Arch P. Dooley, "Interpretations of PERT," *Harvard Business Review,* 42, No. 2, March–April 1964, pp. 161–170.

```
        Set table      Make OJ      Fry bacon   Scramble eggs  Make toast
START o——————→o——————→o——————→o——————→o——————→o EAT
         6 min          3            12            4             4
```

Figure 2.3 Series ordering of an important managerial operation; 29 minutes required.

Other constraints are:

    a.   The table must be set before serving the food.

    b.   The eggs are not to be scrambled first because bacon grease is needed to cook them.

    c.   To mix and pour the orange juice requires continuous operator supervision, as does setting the table; other operations are load and unload.

    d.   Hot items should arrive together if possible.

Figure 2.3 shows the series completion of tasks. It takes 29 minutes to prepare breakfast in this fashion, and the eggs and bacon are cold. Figure 2.4 shows a first attempt to operate in parallel. Notice three tasks are scheduled to originate at once, which may be confusing to the operator, and the eggs will still be cold. But now the longest path is 13 minutes, which is a considerable savings in time. The longest path is called the *critical path*. It is this series of jobs that places the limit on how rapidly the overall task can be brought to completion. The

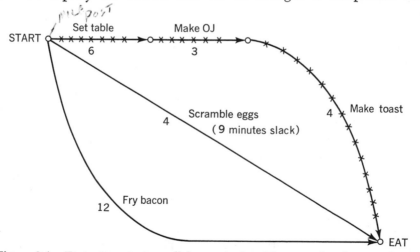

Figure 2.4. First attempt at parallel organization. The critical path is emphasized and is 13 minutes long.

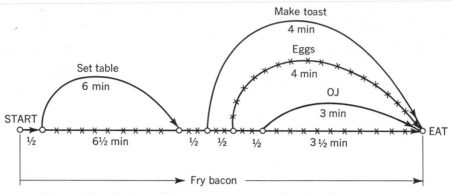

Figure 2.5.   Final parallel organization; critical path is 12 minutes long.

other paths have *float* or *slack* in them. There is a float of 9 minutes in one path and 1 minute in the other.

In Figure 2.5 the scheduling is brought to the irreducible minimum of 12 minutes. "Fry bacon" is now the critical path. Note also that two tasks are never initiated simultaneously and that one slack variable, "set table," is not critical whereas the other, "make toast," is critical [see item (d)] and has only a half-minute slack. It is difficult to say if this little exercise is realistic or not, but if it is, there is one surprise. Most cooks would start with "fry bacon" and then "set table," but the start of "make orange juice" occurs later than one might expect.

The use of an organizational chart such as PERT or CPM not only helps in efficient ordering of subtasks and in estimating completion times, but it also places in evidence those elements that are prospective bottlenecks and to which special attention should be given. Overtime can be scheduled for exactly those elements that will shorten completion time, and delivery of parts and raw materials can be set in an orderly fashion.

Estimation of each subtask time is a critical element in this whole procedure. Some group leaders will add a cushion to protect themselves if you ask them to estimate the time to do a subtask. On the other hand, salesmen chronically underestimate the length of time to complete an overall project for which they want a purchase order. One of the features of PERT is that such vagaries are taken into consideration. Rather than one time estimate, each subtask leader is asked for three time estimates.

t_o = optimistic time estimate. Assume everything goes perfectly.
t_a = average time estimate. Assume the usual number of minor delays.

t_p = pessimistic time estimate. Assume that all the things that can go wrong will.

The designers of PERT noticed that the distribution of these time estimates often took the shape of a *Beta distribution*. Therefore they elected to use the relation for the most likely time or *expected time* t_e given by this distribution.

$$t_e = \frac{1}{6}(t_o + 4t_a + t_p)$$

The expected time is placed on the PERT diagram or sometimes the three estimates themselves are entered.

In evaluating the performance of production or construction jobs there is little difficulty in positively identifying the point in time when a sub-task begins or finishes. These points are called *mile posts*. In research and development, however, there is often little objective evidence that one phase has been completed and another begun. Therefore, mile posts must be chosen with considerable care. Such events as "understanding of goal" or "decision to proceed" are not suitable as mile posts. An objective action such as "oral presentation of material" or "report mailed" is suitable.

PERT and CPM are not substitutes for hard work and good management. Rather, they are aids in organizing the approach to complex decisions given these other factors.

PROBLEMS

2.1   In the organization chart below, find the critical path and identify the slack in other paths. One simple way to do this is to progressively reduce the time elapsing in the critical path until it is no longer critical. Is the chart correctly drawn? that is, could any of the nodes be eliminated?

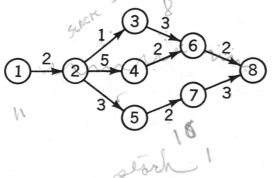

2.2   The unit estimates for house construction are as follows:

UNIT	TIME IN WEEKS	OVERTIME POSSIBLE
Draw plans	4	No
Excavation	½	No
Foundation	1	No
Framework	2	Yes
Rough heating and plumbing	3	Yes
Roofing and siding	2	Yes
Brick veneer	2	Yes
Electrical wiring	1	Yes
Lath and plaster	3	Yes
Outside painting	1½	Yes
Finish floors and cabinet work	3	Yes
Interior paint and paper	3	Yes
Install plumbing fixtures	1	Yes
Install electric fixtures	1	Yes
Seeding and landscaping	1½	Yes

TRADE	SIZE OF GANG	HOURLY RATE PER WORKER
Carpenter	5	$3.50
Laborer	2	$2.50
Mason	4	$4.00
Plumber	1 (plus helper)	$5.00
Electrician	1 (plus helper)	$5.00
Plasterer	2 (plus helper)	$3.50
Painter	2 (plus helper)	$4.50
Gardener and tractor	1 (plus helper)	$6.00

Note: All helpers are paid at laborer's rate. For those jobs on which overtime is possible, the work gang can also be doubled to half the time.

a.   Draw a schedule chart and identify the critical path.

b.   On which units would you apply overtime or doubled work gangs to complete work one week early? Two weeks? Three?

c.   What are the comparative labor costs for each schedule?

CHAPTER THREE

Numerical and Graphical Data Reduction

3.1 INTRODUCTION

Data reduction can be defined as the processing of raw experimental data so as to emphasize and reveal the critical relationships among the physical parameters of the system under study. Data reduction ranges from the simplest form of merely recording a dial reading on a piece of paper to the extremely complicated processing of the raw numbers for months on a mammoth digital computer. A man reporting his golf score is an example of the former (although significant additional "data reduction" sometimes has been known to occur here), and the latter is exemplified by the recent processing of the radar return signals from

Venus. Here the noise was ten thousand times as strong as the expected signal, and months of correlation studies were required before there was any assurance that a signal actually had been received.

In this chapter we will discuss a few of the common problems that arise in handling engineering data, both numerical and graphical. Statistics will be introduced in Chapter 4. Thus Chapters 3 and 4 should aid the experimenter in properly posing a question about nature as well as interpreting and reporting the answer.

3.2 ACCURACY AND PRECISION

Accuracy and precision are not synonymous. Precision has to do with the dependability or reproducibility of a certain measurement whereas accuracy refers to the correctness with which a certain reading represents the true value. This may seem vague, so let us see if we can further explain these two concepts. The number we write down is an *indicated value* that represents a hypothetical *true value*. The indicated value may be somewhat greater or somewhat less than the true value. The *range* of the indicated value is its *precision*. For example, suppose the indicated value is 1.0 and the range of precision of the indicated value is ±0.05. This means that each time a measurement is taken the indicated value[1] is less than 1.05 but more than 0.95.

This does not tell us, however, where the true value lies. Whereas precision refers to the width of the range of the indicated values, *accuracy* is defined as the correctness with which a given range indicates the true value. Taking these two concepts together means, for example, that we could have a very precise (narrow range) indicated value that at the same time could be quite inaccurate. This could come about if the indicating instrument were not properly *calibrated* or adjusted before use. Some precise measuring devices contain within them a means of internal calibration. Internal calibration usually permits adjusting the mechanism so that the reading is relatively accurate at one, or at most two, points on the scale. True calibration requires that the measuring device be compared with a known standard throughout its range and that a graph be prepared showing the deviation. For obvious reasons this graph is called a *calibration curve*. The adjustment of measuring

[1] There are more sophisticated ways of denoting the scatter of indicated values than range. We will consider several of them in Chapter 4 on statistics.

instruments is a specialized skill requiring reference instruments that are more precise and more accurately calibrated than the instrument under adjustment. For these reasons it is common practice to return instruments to the factory for calibration and adjustment.

Note that a precise but inaccurate instrument indicates a *systematic error* or *bias* of some kind. Systematic errors, once discovered, can be adjusted for in the data reduction process. It is much better practice, of course, to have foreseen and eliminated such errors in the first place. An imprecise but accurate series of measurements of a particular value, on the other hand, indicates a *random error* of some sort. It is not possible to correct or eliminate a random error from a single piece of data. However, by *smoothing* or *averaging* over many measurements, it is possible to recover significant amounts of information. Random errors have many causes. Generally speaking, they can be traced to one or more uncontrolled variables in the experiment. It is impossible to control all variables, especially in an experiment carried out under actual operating conditions in the field. Therefore proper data reduction by the application of the principles of probability and statistics is important to the engineer. A mistake is another matter entirely. A *mistake* is an improper act of omission or commission by the experimenter. If a datum point falls far from the remainder of the data because an improper scale was read by the observer, this is a mistake and can be eliminated from the tabulation if it is discovered.

3.3 SIGNIFICANT FIGURES AND ROUND-OFF ERROR

"The table on this scale says for my height I should weigh 185 pounds, so I am two and a half pounds under weight." Does this statement make engineering sense? How about this one? "I weighed myself on this scale before breakfast yesterday, and overnight I have lost about two pounds." Probably the first statement is nonsense and the second debatable, although on different grounds (accuracy versus precision). At the risk of making what seems to be a perfectly simple problem ridiculously complex, here are a few of the items involved in the first statement.

1. The population for which the table is computed: Large or small boned people? Men or women? With or without clothes? Before or after eating or exercise?

2. The accuracy and precision of the scale: Is this a bathroom scale? A truck scale down at the lumber yard?

3. The measurement error: Are you standing on the center of the scale platform? Are the temperature and humidity conditions within the range for which the scale is calibrated?

4. The reading error: Is the scale divided to the nearest pound? If the smallest division is 5 pounds, can you read to the nearest half pound? Have you compensated for parallax?

We will consider a number of instrumentation problems in this book. Here we wish to consider one involved in the number of significant figures. Suppose the scale mentioned above is guaranteed to be accurate to 0.50 percent of full-scale reading, which happens to be 250 pounds. This is 1.25 pounds, and there would be doubt about the last two figures of a scale reading of, say, 182.6 pounds. The 0.6 is without foundation, and we are constrained to round off to 183 pounds. This is still three significant figures and is probably not justified in a nonprecise experiment. Actually it is difficult to believe that better than two-place accuracy (precision is another matter) can be obtained in any uncontrolled experiment such as this. Therefore we should report the weight to perhaps the nearest 5 pounds; however, let us accept the three-place figure during the calculation. Now subtract 183 from the "standard" of 185 pounds (the meaning of which remains unclear, of course).

$$
\begin{array}{r}
185 \text{ pounds standard} \\
- \ 183 \text{ pounds scale reading} \\
\hline
2 \text{ pounds difference}
\end{array}
$$

Notice that although the original data for this subtraction were significant to three figures, the result is accurate to only one. Subtraction of two large approximately equal numbers is perhaps the most notorious source of loss of accuracy in the entire field of numerical analysis, but, as we shall see, all computations require care.

The number of significant figures in a reading indicates the precision of the measurement. Suppose, for example, that the output of a tachometer is in the form of an electric voltage that is passed through a precision amplifier. (See Figure 3.1.) And suppose that each of these elements can be relied on for three significant figure precision, which is at least one more significant figure than would be obtained in ordinary industrial

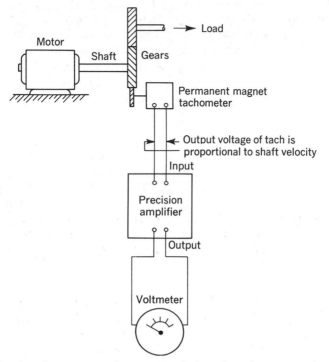

Figure 3.1. A tachometer speed-measuring device; the voltmeter can be calibrated to read in revolutions per minute (RPM) of motor.

practice. Let us find the output voltage from the amplifier for a particular shaft speed.

$$
\begin{array}{ll}
\text{Tachometer reading} & 1.23 \text{ volts} \\
\text{Amplifier gain} & \times\ 155 \\
\hline
& 190.65 \text{ volts}
\end{array}
$$

Now, even though each element has at best three-figure significance, the final number has been given to five significant figures. This obviously is nonsense, and the result should be rounded to three significant figures or 191 volts.

The number of significant figures in an observation has nothing to do with the magnitude of the number. The number 3425 is less significant than 1.0054 but is more significant than 1.05. The number of significant figures is sometimes difficult to determine unless the so-called *scientific notation* or *powers of ten notation* is used. For example, what are the significant figures in the following list?

$$123,000$$
$$123,000.0$$
$$0.012300$$
$$.0123$$

Doubts can be resolved by rewriting these numbers using the following rule. Move the decimal point to the right or left until a number between one and ten remains to the left of the decimal point; then multiply the result by 10 raised to a power that depends on the places moved. The power is a number (positive if the decimal is moved left and negative if moved right) equal to the number of places moved. Only significant figures are then retained in the powers of ten notation. The following gives some examples.

$123,000 = 1.23 \times 10^5$ three significant figures
$123,000.0 = 1.230000 \times 10^5$ seven significant figures
$0.012300 = 1.2300 \times 10^{-2}$ five significant figures
$.0123 = 1.23 \times 10^{-2}$ three significant figures

Note that in the first item it would have been impossible to indicate four significant figures or five without the powers of ten notation. The powers of ten notation is also essential in calculations that involve a wide range of numbers because otherwise keeping track of the decimal becomes a chore.

The rule for rounding off to a given number of significant figures is to add one unit to the digit in the last significant place if the digit to the right is larger than five (and omit the nonsignificant digits) and to leave the figure in the last significant place unchanged if the next is less than five. If the digit following the last significant place is a 5, leave the last significant digit unchanged if the last significant digit is even, and add one to it if it is odd. Furthermore, in this special case, we round off one digit at a time. For example, round off 1255 to two significant figures. First round to 1260 then to 1300. It would be incorrect to round 1255 to 1200.

The general question of the accuracy of approximate calculations is far from trivial, and J. B. Scarborough thinks the whole subject should be left alone rather than spending only two or three hours on it.[2] Although Scarborough doubtless is infinitely more qualified than I, it appears that a little knowledge, modestly applied, cannot help but be of service.

The following rules (which are culled from Scarborough) apply in handling significant figures in fundamental arithmetic operations.

Addition

Round off all figures to one more decimal place than the absolutely accurate decimal place of the least accurate line before adding. The final result will be in doubt in the final place. Note that absolute not relative accuracy is required here because adding (say, 7 to 7.0×10^7) does not change the original figure.

Subtraction

Round off to same number of absolute decimal places before subtraction (one more than the poorest figure). If the original numbers are approximately equal in magnitude *all* significant figures may be lost. Subtraction should be avoided if possible by alternate forms of computation.

Multiplication and Division

Round off the more accurate number to one more significant figure than the less accurate number. After performing calculations, round off the final result to the same number of significant figures as the poorer of the original figures.

Powers and Roots

For a number with n significant digits the pth power is correct to $n - 2$ figures, and its kth root is correct to $n - 1$ figures. See Scarbor-

[2] J. B. Scarborough, *Numerical Mathematical Analysis*, 5 ed. (Baltimore, Md.: The Johns Hopkins Press, 1962), p. 40.

ough for conditions under which each of these calculations can be improved by one digit.[3]

Logs and Antilogs

If a log table with sufficient places is used, there need be no loss of accuracy in taking the logarithm. However, the antilog of a log correct to m significant figures will be correct to only $m - 1$ significant figures.

General Rules

1. Before beginning computation, round off original data to one more decimal digit (addition and subtraction) or one more significant figure (others) than the poorest number. Do *not* round off again during computation. Present final result to only the same number of significant figures as poorest original data.

2. With only one exception, common computations cannot yield more accurate results than the original data. The exception is averaging a number of data points recorded for repeated observations of the same parameter in which the variation is random rather than systematic. The improvement in accuracy is limited only by the number of measurements taken.

3. Rounding off by digital computer differs from our discussion above. All digits after the maximum number allowed by the machine are simply lost. Thus this process is sometimes distinguished by the term *chop off* or *truncation*.[4] This can result in one less place precision than if the methods discussed above are used.

EXAMPLE 3.1

It is suspected that the main fan pump of a paper-making machine has a worn packing and is leaking excessively to a concealed pump. The plant engineer does not want to shut down the paper machine to check the pump and lose a day's production if he can help it. Can you decide what the leakage is by making a materials' balance? For a particular operating condition, the input flows to the pump are measured by flow meters of

---

[3] Scarborough (see footnote 2).
[4] A more usual use of the word truncation is to indicate the error involved in representing by a finite number of terms, the value of an infinite series.

different types and different accuracies. The input flow from the Jordans basis-weight control is 4.20×10^2 gal/min. The recycle flow into the pump from the cleaner that does not go to the head box is 1.1×10^3 gal/min. The return from the wire pit into the pump is 4735 gal/min to three significant figures, and the total outflow from the pump is 6250 gal/min to three significant figures.

As a first method of calculation, round all inlet flows to three significant figures, since this is one more than the poorest of the group and add all inlet flows. Then subtract the outlet flow from the result to find the leakage.

Method I

FACTORS			FLOW READINGS (IN GAL/MIN)	ROUNDED
Wire pit	(3 sig. fig.)	=	4735	4740
Cleaners	(2 sig. fig.)	=	1100	1100
Jordans	(3 sig. fig.)	=	420	420
Total inlet		=		6260
Total outlet		=	−6250	−6250
Leakage		=		10

The result is 10 gal/min leakage. Now we will subtract each input individually from the output flow and retain one more significant figure than the poorer of the two figures at each step.

Method II

FACTORS			FLOW READINGS (IN GAL/MIN)
Output	(3 sig. fig.)	=	6250
−Wirepit	(3 sig. fig.)	=	−4735
Subtotal		=	1515
Round off to		=	1520
−Cleaners	(2 sig. fig.)	=	−1100
Subtotal		=	420
−Jordans	(3 sig. fig.)	=	−420
Leakage		=	0

Now suppose we round off all data to two significant figures, since that is all the cleaner flow is good to, and repeat Methods I and II.

Method III

FACTORS		FLOW READINGS (IN GAL/MIN)
Wirepit	=	4700
Cleaners	=	1100
Jordans	=	420
Total inlet	=	6220
−Outlet	=	−6200
Leakage	=	20

Method IV

FACTORS		FLOW READINGS (IN GAL/MIN)
Output	=	6200
−Wirepit	=	−4700
Subtotal	=	1500
−Cleaners	=	−1100
Subtotal	=	400
−Jordans	=	−420
		− 20

Now repeat without rounding off at all.

Method V

FACTORS		FLOW READINGS (IN GAL/MIN)
Wirepit	=	4735
Cleaners	=	1100
Jordans	=	420
Total inlet	=	6255
−Outlet	=	−6250
Leakage	=	5

One can take a choice of any of these answers since they are all meaningless anyway. The maximum absolute error of a number is one half a unit in the last significant figure. This will be apparent if you think of the rule for rounding off. Thus, the maximum error in the initial reading of cleaner flow is 50 gal/min. Probably Method I and Method V yield better answers than do the other three methods, but the final figures used in the calculation could vary and we will leave it for the reader to show that the actual result could lie anywhere between 66 gal/min leakage out of the pump to 56 gal/min leakage *into* the pump. With these data we are positive that it is impossible to tell the plant engineer if the packing leaks. You have been led down the garden path by this example. You could have proved the exercise was useless by this reasoning before we started.

3.4 PROPAGATION OF ERRORS[5]

Although the general study of propagation of errors is beyond the level of this text, we can illustrate the effect on errors of common arithmetic operations. Consider two numbers $A + a$ and $B + b$. In each case the capital letter represents the true value, and the lower case letter represents the error. Both the true value and the error can be either positive or negative quantities, but we will assume that the error is small with respect to the true value, that is, $|a| \ll |A|$ and $|b| \ll |B|$.

The error involved in *addition and subtraction* may be seen by writing

$$(A + a) + (B + b) = (A + B) + (a + b)$$

Thus the absolute error of the sum is the sum of the errors of the components. If A and B are almost equal in magnitude and opposite in sign, the relative error $(a + b)/(A + B)$ of the sum can be very large even though the original absolute errors a and b were quite small with respect to their respective true values of A and B.

The error involved in *multiplication* is

$$(A + a)(B + b) = AB + aB + bA + ab$$

Because of the original assumption of small absolute error components, the term ab is tiny with respect to either aB or bA and may be neglected.

[5] This section follows P. Calingaert, *Principles of Computation* (Reading, Mass.: Addison-Wesley Publishing Company, Inc., 1965), Section 5.2.

The relative error is approximately

$$\frac{aB + bA}{AB} = \frac{a}{A} + \frac{b}{B}$$

and the absolute error in the product is approximately $aB + bA$.
Division yields

$$\frac{A + a}{B + b} = \frac{A + a}{B(1 + b/B)} = \frac{A + a}{B}\left[1 - \frac{b}{B} + \left(\frac{b}{B}\right)^2 \cdots\right]$$

The $(b/B)^2$ and successive terms may be neglected. Thus we have

$$\frac{A + a}{B + b} \simeq \frac{A + a}{B}\left(1 - \frac{b}{B}\right) = \frac{A}{B} + \frac{a}{B}\left(1 - \frac{b}{B}\right) - \frac{Ab}{B^2}$$

The absolute error is

$$\frac{a}{B}\left(1 - \frac{b}{B}\right) - \frac{Ab}{B^2} \simeq \frac{a}{B} - \frac{Ab}{B^2}$$

Thus a small divisor B yields a large absolute error. The relative error
is

$$\left(\frac{a}{B} - \frac{Ab}{B^2}\right)\Big/\frac{A}{B} = \frac{a}{A} - \frac{b}{B}$$

Of course since the values of all these symbols can be positive or negative, we cannot conclude that the error components cancel. *Powers,
exponentials, and logarithms* will be left for the reader to examine.

3.5   GRAPHS

Graphs are perhaps the most important means of engineering communication. Bar graphs, pie charts, and various other pictorial presentations are common in nontechnical presentations, but the engineer relies
almost exclusively on line graphs. The *line graph* is a smooth curve
that represents the relationship or function between the independent
variable plotted along the horizontal axis or abscissa and the dependent
variable plotted along the vertical axis or ordinate. A relationship which

connects one number of a pair with the other element of the pair is called a *function*. The functional relationship between x and y, $y = f(x)$, can be analytic or graphical.

The beginning student will have every right to feel confused when he compares the explicit directions for properly constructing a graph given below and the hundreds of examples he can find in engineering textbooks. Seldom will he find a properly constructed graph in an engineering text. The reasons for this are several. First and foremost is the fact that the curves in engineering texts generally are not used for illustrating as exactly as possible a functional relationship between two variables in a specific experiment. Rather, they are used merely to illustrate the general form or shape of a relation. Second, the problem of clarity in a printed text results in certain omissions such as cross rulings. Third, the cost of space in a text often results in distortions and broken scales. Thus the graphs in typical engineering textbooks cannot be used as a guide for constructing graphs for engineering reports.

Here are ten points to remember in constructing a graph.

1. Establish axes far enough away from the edge of the cross ruling to permit labeling. Do not label in the nonruled margin of the sheet.

2. Label axes completely with the names of the variables and their units or dimensions.

3. Choose a convenient scale for each axis, and label the scale. It may be necessary to try several scales before a satisfactory one is found. Do not break the scale or change the scale along an axis. If for some reason a small portion of the plot is of special interest, follow the general plot with a special plot of that area.

4. Plot the data points as accurately as possible.

5. The confidence interval or variance (defined below) in the data points should be shown with a vertical bar through the datum point or with a circle around it. If a confidence interval is not given, the data cannot be presumed to be significant at all.

6. In the absence of any known physical law that governs the relationship between the two variables, a smooth curve should be passed through, or at least near, each datum point. At times the data are so scattered that a curve passing near each point would contain many inflections. This sometimes indicates that the accuracy and/or the precision of the data is suspect and more data should be gathered. At times one datum point lies some distance away from a smooth curve that passes near all the other points. Here again more data should be

gathered.[6] These are two excellent reasons for plotting the data points as they are gathered in the laboratory. One more reason for immediate plotting is that an approximate value for the next datum point to be gathered can be established, and the scale factors in the indicating instruments can be adjusted in advance.

7. If a particular physical law for the data has been postulated, a least-square fit of this law to the data should be employed in drawing the smooth curve and this fact noted in the legend.

8. A complete and meaningful title should be centrally located on the sheet.

9. The nameplate data or complete description of the device under test and the legend, if more than one curve is plotted, should be contained in a box on the sheet. It is sometimes advisable to show a block diagram of the measurement procedure on the sheet if the method is not standard.

10. Date and sign the plot in small but legible letters.

3.6 GRAPHICAL SOLUTION OF SIMULTANEOUS EQUATIONS

Graphical aids to computation are often used by the engineer. Graphical solution of a nonlinear differential equation, for example, may be the most practical means of gaining an insight into its behavior even if a computer is ultimately to be used. Also, the solution of simultaneous equations is often easily carried out graphically. A further use of graphical techniques may occur when an equation of a given form must repeatedly be solved for various values of parameters. In order to save time, a special-purpose slide rule may be constructed or even a special-purpose computer built. However, a much simpler technique is to construct a *nomograph* or *alignment chart*. We will give examples of the latter two applications and leave the graphical solution of nonlinear differential equations for a later course.

EXAMPLE 3.2   GRAPHICAL SOLUTION OF SIMULTANEOUS EQUATIONS

Suppose you have a Model A that you have worked over but which really will not go fast. Someone offers to sell you a new engine to re-

---

[6] The troublesome point should *not* be omitted from the plot unless a mistake is known to have been made.

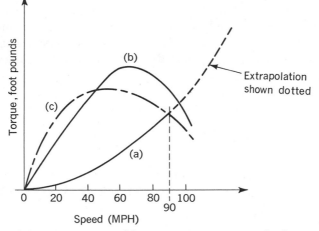

Figure 3.2.   (*a*)   Torque required by an auto at various speeds, determined by road test data.
(*b*)   Torque supplied by new engine at full throttle.
(*c*)   Torque supplied by present V-8 engine at full throttle.

place the old V-8 you now have in there. Could you compute the new top speed before doing any work or spending any money? The answer is Yes, if the speed-torque curve of the new engine is available.

In Chapter 6 we will discuss the method of computing from road-test data the force or torque needed to sustain an automobile at any given speed. You can use this method to find the torque required for your Model A at a number of speeds and plot a curve of torque required versus speed. This plus the data on the new engine are all that you need.

In Figure 3.2, curve (*a*) shows the torque computed for the Model A by using road-test data. The point at 90 mph is as high as the present rig will go. Thus the curve is *extrapolated* or extended by estimation, as shown by the dotted portion. Now when curve (*b*) for the new engine is superimposed, you find an intersection of the torque needed by the automobile, and the torque provided by the new engine at about 97 mph. This is the only point (other than standstill) at which torque developed equals torque required.

Now you can make your decision to buy the new engine or not. Simply because we all like to talk about cars, I will mention one more point. You might have been surprised at the result shown in Figure 3.2 because the new engine was listed at a much higher horsepower than your present mill. Curve (*c*) shows the speed-torque curve of the old V-8 presently in the car. It has higher torque at lower speeds, and you

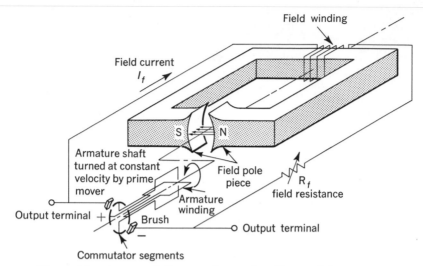

Figure 3.3. A pictorial diagram of a simple self-excited dc generator.

would actually *lose* acceleration by installing the new engine. The new engine torque peaks up at a higher speed, and since the product of speed and torque is proportional to horsepower, the new engine may seem like a good deal but probably is not.

This example of graphical solution of simultaneous relations illustrates a case in which an analytic or mathematical solution is impossible because the original data are given graphically.

EXAMPLE 3.3   GRAPHICAL SOLUTION OF SIMULTANEOUS EQUATIONS

Often in electric and hydraulic circuits, certain circuit elements are described by nonlinear relationships. This is true for hydraulic flow versus pressure in orifices and for electric current versus voltage in electronic tubes and transistors. Figure 3.3 shows another common example. This figure shows a simplified form of a self-excited dc generator. A current flowing into the field winding causes a magnetic field through which the armature winding is turned. A fundamental law of physics[7] states that a

---

[7] We will be using phrases such as "fundamental law of physics" and "basic law of thermodynamics" rather frequently in this course. Let us make two observations about this sort of thing at the outset. First, the phrase generally means that you will find the law discussed in detail in a later engineering course. Second, even though the so-called basic law may be derived from even more basic principles, eventually these laws are based on observed natural phenomena.

conductor moving through a magnetic field has a voltage induced on it. The magnitude of the voltage depends on the length of the conductor, the strength of the magnetic field, and the velocity of the conductor with respect to the magnetic field (Biot's law). The armature in Figure 3.3 is the moving conductor. The commutator segments and brushes serve two purposes. First, some sort of sliding connection is necessary if the armature wires are not to be wrapped around the shaft as it is turned. Second, as an individual armature conductor passes up through the magnetic field and then around and down again, the voltage induced in it is first of one polarity then the other. The commutator switches the brush from one wire to the next so that the voltage at a particular brush always remains of one polarity. The terminals are connected to the brushes, and the voltage induced in the armature is thus available for useful work at the output terminals. Lights, motors, or any other sort of electrical load may be connected across the output terminals of the generator. At a later point we will return to this device to discuss the flow of energy· through it from the "prime mover" to the electrical load.

Note in Figure 3.3, that in addition to supplying an external load, the generator is expected to supply its own field circuit. If you are saying to yourself that this sort of "bootstrap" operation is impossible, you are wrong; you are equally wrong if you are thinking that obviously it will work. You should suspend judgment until you have analyzed the operation of the device. In this case, analysis is not too difficult, but often analysis of the stability of operating points is the source of many interesting problems of an advanced nature.

In order to establish the operation of the self-excited generator, two laws, rules, or equations must be satisfied. The law of induced or generated voltage must be satisfied in the armature, and Ohm's law must be satisfied in the field circuit. This is diagramed in Figure 3.4. The functional relationship of current and voltage in the field circuit is linear and is given by Ohm's law. The functional relation between generated voltage and field current is more complex. First, we know that the generated voltage really is a function of wire length and shaft velocity as well as magnetic field strength and perhaps other things such as temperature. Second there is the detailed relation between field current and magnetic field strength.

Although it is possible by many steps to calculate all of those things, it seems most direct to measure experimentally the relationship between field current and terminal voltage. As shown in Figure 3.5(a), the procedure is to discount the field circuit from the armature and to force a current from an external source through the field. Then record the field current and terminal voltage. The result is far from a straight line. The desired relationship is $V_t = f_2(I_f)$, provided all other parameters were held constant during the experiment. You might speculate, for example,

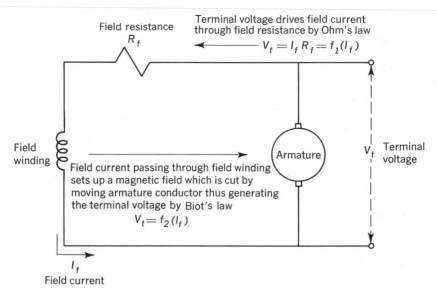

Figure 3.4. Diagram of simultaneous relations to be satisfied by self-excited dc generator.

on the shape of the curve if the experiment were repeated at 20 percent reduction in prime mover speed.

Since $V_t = f_2(I_f)$ is known graphically and does not appear susceptible to a simple analytic approximation, it seems that solution of f_1 and f_2 simultaneously for the operating point should be done graphically. In Figure 3.5(b), f_1 is plotted for $R_f = 33.3$ Ω. Now since f_2 is plotted on the same axes, an intersection of the two curves indicates a simultaneous solution of the two relations and a possible operating point for the generator.

We should not leave this example without drawing a few conclusions.[8] Note that our graphical approach to the problem bypasses a number of detailed calculations. In addition, note how easy it is to resolve the problem for a different value of field resistance or if the shaft speed is changed. In fact, we can now choose the proper value of field resistance for a desired terminal voltage. This then becomes an example of engineering *design* or *synthesis* as opposed to *analysis*. In analysis we are given all the

---

[8] Sometimes your instructor will ask you to draw your own conclusions from his examples. You must continually ask yourself (or your instructor), "What is the point of all this?" You have gained very little from an educational experience of any kind if you cannot draw general conclusions.

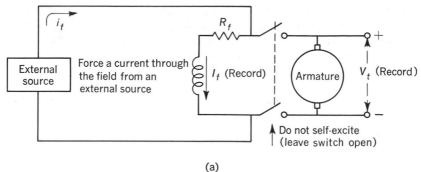

(a)

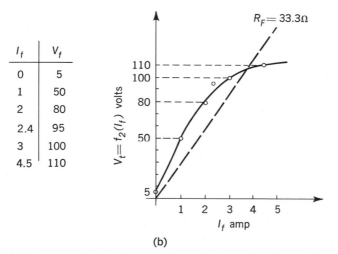

(b)

Figure 3.5. Diagram of experimental determination of relation between field current, I_f, and terminal voltage, V_t, in a dc generator.

parts and asked for the result. In the more realistic and interesting synthesis problem, we are asked to pick one or more of the parts of a system so as to make the system meet certain specifications.

Finally, we observe that this graphical approach permits an insight into the *sensitivity* of the operating point to small changes in parameter values. Suppose, for example, that R_f were approximately 50Ω. Then a change of ±1 Ω would change the terminal voltage between about 20 V and 80 V. In other words, a 4-percent change in field resistance causes a 400-percent change in terminal voltage. Such a condition is called *structurally unstable* and is not acceptable as an engineering solution. Note that if the function plots cross at right angles, the sensitivity of the solution to slight parameter changes is minimized, and it becomes larger as the functions approach parallelism. An engineer should strive for minimum sensitivity and maximum structural stability in his designs.

3.7   NOMOGRAPHS

Graphical solutions of equations with any number of variables in any functional form is possible if it is possible in theory. We have chosen to illustrate the philosophy with a fairly common form. The parallel-scale nomograph for equations of three variables is most directly applied to equations of the forms:

$$f_1(u) + f_2(v) = f_3(w) \tag{3.1}$$

and

$$f_1(u)f_2(v) = f_3(w) \tag{3.2}$$

where two of the variables are given and the third is sought. For a general treatment of more complex forms of nomographs, see L. H. Johnson.[9]

As shown in Figure 3.6, the problem is to position the w-scale with respect to the u-scale and the v-scale and to determine the proper scale modulus. Obviously, these things depend on the original choice of the u-scale and the v-scale. Consider an equation of the form of Equation (3.1). Select a sheet of paper, and construct the u-scale and the v-scale parallel and with a convenient (arbitrary) spacing. Next it will be neces-

[9] L. H. Johnson, *Nomography and Empirical Equations* (New York: John Wiley and Sons, Inc., 1952).

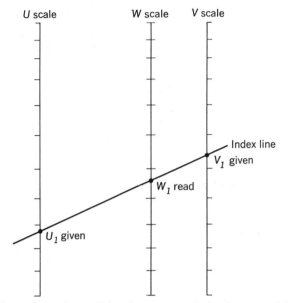

Figure 3.6. A parallel-scale nomograph for three variables.

sary to relate the scale of the paper to the scale of the physical variables. We will do this with relations of the following form.

u-scale: x (paper units) $= m_1 \left(\dfrac{\text{paper units}}{\text{functional units}} \right) f_1(u)$ (functional units)

$$(3.3)$$

v-scale: y (paper units) $= m_2 \left(\dfrac{\text{paper units}}{\text{functional units}} \right) f_2(v)$ (functional units)

$$(3.4)$$

w-scale: z (paper units) $= m_3 \left(\dfrac{\text{paper units}}{\text{functional units}} \right) f_3(w)$ (functional units)

$$(3.5)$$

The moduli m_1 and m_2 are chosen to make the u-scale and the v-scale fit conveniently on the paper. Next the w-scale will be erected parallel to the others. Its spacing will be determined by the derivation, and the modulus m_3 of the w-scale will be determined by calculations.

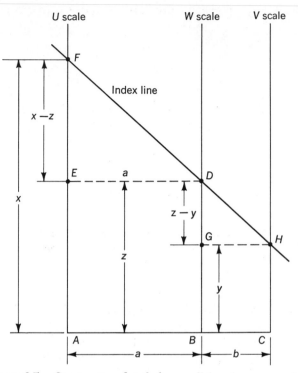

Figure 3.7. Construction details for parallel scale nomograph.

Let ABC be the base line and a and b the distances between scales as shown in Figure 3.7. Draw any index line FH, not parallel to ABC. Form the similar triangles DEF and DGH. From these similar triangles we have

$$\frac{x - z}{a} = \frac{z - y}{b} \tag{3.6}$$

Thus

$$bx + ay = (a + b)z$$

and dividing by ab yields

$$\frac{x}{a} + \frac{y}{b} + \frac{(a + b)}{ab}\, z = \frac{z}{ab/(a + b)} \tag{3.7}$$

Now substituting the particular functions for x, y, and z from Equations (3.3), (3.4), and (3.5), we have

$$\frac{m_1 f_1(u)}{a} + \frac{m_2 f_2(v)}{b} = \frac{m_3 f_3(w)}{ab/(a+b)} \tag{3.8}$$

We ask now what are the conditions for which Equation (3.8) reduces to Equation (3.1). Apparently this happens if

$$a = m_1; \qquad b = m_2$$

$$\frac{ab}{a+b} = m_3 = \frac{m_1 m_2}{m_1 + m_2} \tag{3.9}$$

In fact, a, b, and $ab/(a+b)$ need only be related to m_1, m_2, and m_3 respectively by a constant of proportionality (not necessarily unity), which we will leave for you to show.

EXAMPLE 3.4   PARALLEL SCALE NOMOGRAPH
FOR EQUATION WITH THREE VARIABLES

Suppose we wish to construct a nomograph that will be used to compute the final grade in a course. It is assumed that the final grade is made up by weighting the average of the homework grades by 0.6 and the averaged test grades by 0.4. Let

$$u \triangleq \text{average of homework grades}$$
$$v \triangleq \text{average of test grades}$$
$$w \triangleq \text{final grade}$$

Equation (3.4) for this example becomes

$$0.6u \text{ (percentage points)} + 0.4v \text{ (percentage points)}$$
$$= w \text{ (percentage points)} \tag{3.10}$$

Now erect the u-scale and the v-scale parallel to each other but with arbitrary spacing and a convenient scale, as has been done in Figure 3.8. The phrase "paper unit" is a little clumsy, but we use it rather than an absolute scale such as inches to emphasize the fact the engineer can use any size of paper he pleases. You can follow this discussion by making your own plot, and it would aid your understanding if you were to do so. Simply to illustrate the generality of the procedure, we chose the

u-scale and the v-scale of different lengths. The following three choices are arbitrary. Let

100 percent on the u-scale occupy 40 paper units
100 percent on the v-scale occupy 30 paper units
The spacing between the u-scale and v-scale be 40 paper units

Now calculate m_1 and m_2 using Equations (3.3) and (3.4) and by substituting particular known value pairs for x_1, $f_1(u_1)$ and y_1, $f_2(v_1)$. The most convenient choice here is the full-scale readings. Thus

$$m_1 = \frac{x_1}{f_1(u_1)} = \frac{40 \text{ (paper units)}}{(0.6)(100)(\text{percentage points})} = 0.67 \text{ (paper units/percent)}$$

$$(3.11)$$

and

$$m_2 = \frac{y_1}{f_2(v_1)} = \frac{30 \text{ (paper units)}}{(0.4)(100)(\text{percent})} = 0.75 \text{ (paper units/percent)} \quad (3.12)$$

Using Equation (3.9), m_3 may be calculated as

$$m_3 = \frac{(0.67)(0.75)}{(0.67) + (0.75)} = 0.354 \text{ (paper units/percent)} \quad (3.13)$$

Now calculate the position of the w-scale.

Since
$$a:m_1 \text{ and } b:m_2$$

then
$$a + b:m_1 + m_2$$

and
$$\frac{a}{m_1} = \frac{a + b}{m_1 + m_2}$$

or

$$a = (a + b)\frac{m_1}{m_1 + m_2} = \frac{40(0.67)}{1.42} = 18.9 \text{ (paper units)} \quad (3.14)$$

Now to find the scale of w, we have by Equation (3.13) that $m_3 = 0.354$. Thus by Equation (3.5), at full scale,

$$z = 0.354 \text{ (paper units/percentage points) } 100 \text{ (percent points)}$$
$$z = 35.4 \text{ (paper units)} \quad (3.15)$$

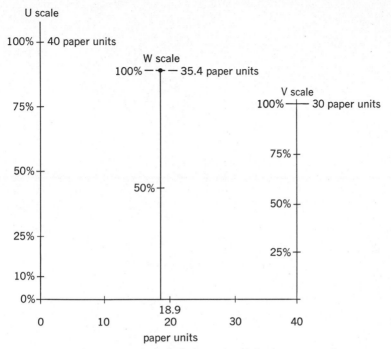

Figure 3.8. Nomograph for computing final course grade.

With Equations (3.14) and (3.15) the construction in Figure 3.8 can be completed. More points along each scale can be computed in the same manner. The reader probably appreciates that this is really only a simple exercise in elementary geometry and that the whole problem could have been done by drawing a few straight lines with a ruler. However, this same appreciative reader has doubtless read the second paragraph of Section 1.5.

3.8 LEAST-SQUARE FIT[10]

Seldom if ever will experimental data conform perfectly to a smooth curve. The engineer is often faced with the task of matching a curve to the given data. Perhaps he knows the form of the curve or has decided arbitrarily on a certain form, but the task of locating the curve with

[10] Scarborough, pp. 446–459 (see footnote 2).

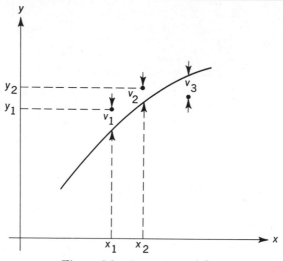

Figure 3.9.   Least-squares fit.

respect to the data remains. The problem is to find the coefficients a, b, c, $\cdots$ of the given equation,

$$y = a + bx + cx^2 + \cdots \qquad (3.16)$$

such that the curve passes as closely as possible to the given data points (x_1, y_1), (x_2, y_2), $\cdots$, (x_n, y_n). (The curve will not necessarily pass through any of the given points.) We will use as a criterion of goodness of fit the sum of the squares of the residuals or vertical differences between the data points and the curve, as shown in Figure 3.9. This is probably the simplest criterion that could be used, since it is obviously not desirable to allow a negative residual to cancel a positive residual. Substitution of the data points into Equation (3.16) will generate the set of residuals

$$
\begin{aligned}
v_1 &= a + bx_1 + cx_1^2 + \cdots - y_1 \\
v_2 &= a + bx_2 + cx_2^2 + \cdots - y_2 \\
&\ \cdot\cdot\cdot\cdot\cdot\cdot\cdot\cdot\cdot\cdot\cdot\cdot\cdot\cdot\cdot\cdot\cdot\cdot\cdot \\
v_n &= a + bx_n + cx_n^2 + \cdots - y_n
\end{aligned}
\qquad (3.17)
$$

Choose a, b, c, $\cdots$ to minimize

$$v_1^2 + \cdots v_n^2 = f(a, b, c, \cdots) \qquad (3.18)$$

Now substituting Equations (3.16) and (3.17) into Equation (3.18) results in

$$
\begin{aligned}
&(a + bx_1 + cx_1{}^2 + \cdots - y_1)^2 \\
&+ (a + bx_2 + cx_2{}^2 + \cdots - y_2)^2 \\
&+ \cdots + (a + bx_n + cx_n{}^2 + \cdots - y_n)^2 \\
&= f(a, b, c, \cdots)
\end{aligned}
\tag{3.19}
$$

which is to be minimized. In order to accomplish this, the various partial derivatives with respect to a, b, c, $\cdots$ must be zero. Then dividing by 2 yields the so-called normal equations:

$$
\begin{aligned}
(a + bx_1 + cx_1{}^2 + \cdots - y_1) &+ (a + bx_2 + cx_2{}^2 + \cdots - y_2) \\
&+ \cdots + (a + bx_n + cx_n{}^2 \\
&+ \cdots - y_n) = 0 \\
x_1(a + bx_1 + cx_1{}^2 + \cdots - y_1) &+ x_2(a + bx_2 + cx_2{}^2 + \cdots - y_2) \\
&+ \cdots + x_n(a + bx_n + cx_n{}^2 \\
&+ \cdots - y_n) = 0 \\
x_1{}^2(a + bx_1 + cx_1{}^2 + \cdots - y_1) &+ x_2{}^2(a + bx_2 + cx_2{}^2 + \cdots - y_2) \\
&+ \cdots + x_n{}^2(a + bx_n + cx_n{}^2 \\
&+ \cdots - y_n) = 0
\end{aligned}
$$

$$\tag{3.20}$$

The normal equations can be solved for the unknown coefficients by the usual algebraic means. There will always be the same number of normal equations as unknowns, but the number of observations must always be greater than the number of undetermined coefficients if the method of least squares is to be of benefit in the solution.

EXAMPLE 3.5

Let us take a simple example to demonstrate the method. Given the values in Table 3.1, find the coefficients of the best second-degree curve to fit these data.

Table 3.1   Data for Least-Square-Fit Example

n	x	y
1	1	1
2	2	3
3	3	5
4	4	7

From Equation (3.20) the normal equations may be found as:

$$4a + 10b + 30c = 16$$
$$10a + 30b + 100c = 50 \qquad\qquad (3.21)$$
$$30a + 100b + 354c = 170$$

It is not difficult by simultaneous solution to find $a = -1$, $b = 2$, and $c = 0$. In fact it is apparent that this is the exact relationship required and that the residuals will be zero. However, as you solve Equation (3.21) you will be impressed with the number of times small differences between large numbers are involved. This situation is rather common in the method and is fraught with computational difficulties. J. B. Scarborough, in discussing this point[11] suggests the following rule: "If the constants are desired to m significant figures and if a preliminary calculation shows that the first p figures will disappear by subtraction, the calculation must be performed with $m + p + 1$ significant figures throughout from beginning to end."

3.9   TECHNICAL AND SCIENTIFIC UNITS:
THE INTERNATIONAL STANDARD (MKSA) SYSTEM

The British system of coinage is a perennial source of amusement to the remainder of the world. The silly arguments the English give about the temporary difficulty of people adjusting themselves to a new decimal system and the cost of coining new tokens persuade almost no one. We would never put up with such a farce in the United States—or would we? Is not our common system of measurement just as silly? Pounds, shillings, and pence or pounds, inches, and horsepower—are they not equally illogical? As a matter of fact, England will have converted to the metric system in measurement (as well as coinage) in the very near future, probably before we in the United States.

The so-called English system of measurement and the CGS system (based on centimeters, grams and seconds) are on the way out. The MKSA units (which are based on the meter, kilogram, second, and ampere) have been adopted by the General Conference of Weights and Measures as the International System of Units (abbreviated SI Units). The six units shown in Table 3.2 are the basis of the system.

[11] Scarborough, p. 439 (see footnote 2).

The official names of multiples and submultiples of units are given in Table 3.3.

Table 3.2   Basic Units of the International System of Units

QUANTITY	NAME	SYMBOL
Length	meter	m
Mass	kilogram	kg
Time	second	s
Electric current	ampere	A
Thermodynamic temperature	Kelvin degree	°K
Luminous intensity	candela	cd

Table 3.3   Table of Multiples and Submultiples

FACTOR BY WHICH UNIT IS MULTIPLIED	PREFIX	SYMBOL
$1\ 000\ 000\ 000\ 000 = 10^{12}$	tera	T
$1\ 000\ 000\ 000 = 10^{9}$	giga	G
$1\ 000\ 000 = 10^{6}$	mega	M
$1\ 000 = 10^{3}$	kilo	k
$100 = 10^{2}$	hecto	h
$10 = 10^{1}$	deka	da
$0.1 = 10^{-1}$	deci	d
$0.01 = 10^{-2}$	centi	c
$0.001 = 10^{-3}$	milli	m
$0.000\ 001 = 10^{-6}$	micro	μ
$0.000\ 000\ 001 = 10^{-9}$	nano	n
$0.000\ 000\ 000\ 001 = 10^{-12}$	pico	p

There is also a number of derived units, most of whose dimensions are obvious. For example, velocity is measured in meters per second, and acceleration has the dimension meters per second per second or meters per second squared. Some derived units are so common, however, that a new shortened name is assigned. For example, force is a unit derived from mass and acceleration by Newton's law:

$$F = MA\,(\text{kg})\,\frac{(\text{m})}{(\text{s}^2)}$$

and thus has the units kilogram meters per second squared. Its shortened
name in SI Units is the newton. Several other derived units and their
names are given in Table 3.4.

Table 3.4   Derived Units in the International System

QUANTITY	UNIT	SYMBOL	REMARKS
Frequency	hertz	Hz	cycles per second
Force	newton	N	$kg \cdot m/s^2$
Pressure (stress)	newton per square meter	N/m^2	
Kinematic viscosity	square meter per second	m^2/s	
Dynamic viscosity	newton second per square meter	$N \cdot s/m^2$	
Work, energy, quantity of heat	joule	J	(not British thermal units)
Power	watt	W	(not horsepower)
Voltage, potential difference, electromotive force	volt	V	
Electric charge	coulomb	C	ampere-seconds
Electric field strength	volt per meter	V/m	
Electric resistance	ohm	Ω	volts per ampere
Capacitance	farad	F	
Magnetic flux	weber	Wb	(not maxwells)
Inductance	henry	H	
Magnetic flux density	tesla	T	weber per meter²
Magnetic field strength	ampere per meter	A/m	(not oersteds)
Magnetomotive force	ampere	A	(not gilberts)
Luminous flux	lumen	lm	(not footcandles)
Luminance	candela per square meter	cd/m^2	(not footlamberts)
Illumination	lux	lx	lumens per square meter

American mechanical engineers are reluctant to give up the horsepower and the Btu (British thermal unit), and electrical engineers are
temporarily uncomfortable with amperes of magnetomotive force and
frequency in hertz as well as the subunit pico. All of us will miss the

pound, the mile, and the Fahrenheit degree. Undoubtedly it will cost money and years to convert completely to metric screw threads and the like, but all parties are interested in a smooth changeover and wish to impose a minimum disturbance during the transition. The changeover would have been easier 20 years ago than it is today, and it is easier today than it will be 20 years from now.[12] A suitable procedure during the interim is that recently adopted by our National Space Agency. All numbers are reported in metric units followed in parentheses by the equivalent in English units.

PROBLEMS

3.1 Express the transcendental number II to eight significant figures. Next round off II to seven significant figures. Repeat until only one significant figure remains.

3.2 Consider the leakage problem with the paper machine. Draw a diagram illustrating the material balance of the flows. Demonstrate that leakage could range from 66 gal/min out to 56 gal/min into the machine given the stated flow data.

3.3 a. Find the expressions for the relative and absolute errors in $(A + a)^n$.
 b. Specifically find the approximate relative, and absolute errors when $n = \frac{1}{2}$.
Hint: Try the binomial series.

3.4 Given a true value A and its associated small error, a, as well as a true value B and its associated small error, b, derive the approximate absolute and relative errors in division of $(A + a)/(B + b)$. Use long division not the series expansion in the text.

---

[12] In evidence we present a resolution adopted at the recent Buffalo meeting of the American Association for the Advancement of Science (AAAS). "Resolved, that the Association welcomes with great satisfaction the recent legislation of Congress authorizing the employment of metric weights and measures, and taking steps facilitating the introducton of the decimal system, and that it congratulates the nation upon this important change, and hopes for further progress in the same direction." August 1866.

3.5 From the data in the table below, plot mortality for various modes of transportation per year. Why do the data for planes show a wider yearly variation than automobiles?

YEAR	CAR	BUS	TRAIN	PLANE
1965	2.4	0.16	0.06	0.38
1964	2.4	0.12	0.05	0.14
1963	2.3	0.23	0.07	0.10
1962	2.3	0.11	0.14	0.30
1961	2.1	0.19	0.10	0.40
1960	2.2	0.13	0.16	1.00
1959	2.3	0.21	0.05	0.70
1958	2.3	0.17	0.27	0.40
1957	2.6	0.19	0.07	0.10
1956	2.7	0.16	0.20	0.60
1955	2.7	0.18	0.07	0.80
1954	2.7	0.11	0.08	0.10
1953	2.9	0.18	0.16	0.60
1952	3.0	0.21	0.04	0.40
1951	3.0	0.24	0.43	1.30
1950	2.9	0.18	0.58	1.10
1949	2.7	0.20	0.08	1.30
1948	2.1	0.18	0.13	1.30
1947	2.3	0.21	0.16	3.20
1946	2.5	0.19	0.18	1.20
1945	2.9	0.17	0.16	2.20
1940	3.5	———	0.34	3.00
1936	4.5	———	0.09	10.00

Fatality rates per 10^8 passenger miles for various modes of transportation in the United States. *Source:* National Safety Council.

3.6 Consider the data given in the table in Figure 3.5. Plot these data properly, and compare with the sketch given. Show the range of precision, vertical and horizontal, for each datum point. Note that the result is not a "circle" around each point but an ellipse.

3.7 Graphically obtain the solution to the following simultaneous equations:

$$y = \frac{1}{x} \quad \text{and} \quad y = 1 + x^2$$

3.8 Plot the magnetization curve for the generator given in Figure 3.5. Find the operating point for $R_f = 20\,\Omega$, $33.3\,\Omega$, and $50\,\Omega$. Repeat the calculation assuming a prime mover speed decrease of 20 percent.

3.9 Demonstrate that the distances a and b between nomograph scales in Figure 3.7 and $ab/(a+b)$ need be proportional but not necessarily equal to m_1, m_2, and m_3.

3.10 Given the following table of values for x and y, find the equation $y = f(x)$, which is the best least-square fit straight line.

x	y
0	2
1	3
2	6
3	7
4	7

3.11 For an experimental propellor-driven hovercraft of unusual design, the thrust T lb of the propellor depends on the air speed S mi/h of the plane in the following manner:

$$T = 200 - 0.5S$$

The aerodynamic drag D lb on the craft depends on the speed in the following manner:

$$D = \frac{S^2}{200}$$

Determine graphically the maximum speed of the craft by simultaneous solution of the equations.

3.12 R. Stone[13] gives an interesting example of the application of graphical and mathematical techniques to determine the growth rate in the number of teachers in a given school system. He makes a number of assumptions in the analysis with which you may or may not agree. Naturally these assumptions should be open for discussion. The assumptions are

    a. The number of graduates per year in a given school system is proportional to the number of teachers in the unit

[13] R. Stone, "Mathematics in the Social Sciences," *Scientific American*, **211**, No. 3, September 1964, pp. 172–176.

b.   The number of new teachers in the system is proportional to the number of graduates (that is, raw material)

c.   The number of teachers lost from the system is a constant proportion of the total number of teachers

1.   We will now seek an equation which relates these factors together. Define the following symbols.

$x \triangleq$ total number of graduates per year in given region (graduates/year)

$y \triangleq$ total number of teachers in region (teachers)

$\Delta y \triangleq$ number of new teachers per year in region normalized to the total number of teachers $\dfrac{(\text{teachers/year})}{(\text{teachers})}$

$\alpha \triangleq$ number of graduates produced per year by each teacher $\dfrac{(\text{graduates/year})}{(\text{teacher})}$

$\beta \triangleq$ proportion of graduates each year who become teachers each year $\dfrac{(\text{teachers/year})}{(\text{graduates/year})} = \dfrac{(\text{teachers})}{(\text{graduates})}$

$\gamma \triangleq$ loss of teachers per year from region for all reasons normalized to total number of teachers $\dfrac{(\text{teachers/year})}{(\text{teachers})}$

$\delta \triangleq$ net growth per year of teachers normalized to total number of teachers $\dfrac{(\text{teachers/year})}{(\text{teachers})}$

Find a relation expressing these assumptions that involves only α, β, γ, and δ.

Plot β versus α for a fixed γ and various growth rates δ.

2.   A second independent relation between α and β will now be established by making several more assumptions. These are

d.   Suppose that α, the efficiency of teachers, is directly proportional to salary.

e.   Suppose that β, the acquisition rate of teachers, is directly proportional to salary.

Define the following additional symbols.

$$k_1 \triangleq \text{efficiency-salary ratio} \frac{(\text{graduates/year})}{(\text{teachers})} \Big/ (\text{dollars/year})$$

$$k_2 \triangleq \text{acquisition rate-salary ratio} \frac{(\text{teachers/graduates})}{(\text{dollars/year})}$$

$$s \triangleq \text{salary (dollars/year)}$$

Find the relation between α and β involving k_1 and k_2. Superimpose this relation for α and β on the hyperbolae obtained in part (1) for several values of k_1 and k_2.

3. Discuss the meaning of these simultaneous relations and whether the assumptions used to obtain them seem reasonable.

3.13 You are employed as an engineer by the Flexishaft Company, and it is your responsibility to correlate data from your customers and suggest to them the correct shaft to solve their particular problem. Part of your work entails the following: Given the speed (r/min) and horsepower (hp) of the customer's motor, find the necessary shaft based on the consideration of the transmitted torque, which in turn will lead to your selection from the company handbook of materials. Problem after problem of this nature would become quite tedious so it is suggested that you use nomography for your solution.

Summary

Construct a nomogram to solve for the torque given revolutions per minute and horsepower.

Relations

$$\text{hp} = \frac{TN}{63,000}, \text{ where } T = \text{in.-lb and } N = \text{rpm.} \tag{1}$$

$$1 \leq T \leq 1000.$$
$$10 \leq N \leq 10,000.$$

Suggested Procedure

1. Take the logarithm of relation (1).
2. Let $\log T = f_1(x)$; $\log N = f_2(y)$; and $\log 63{,}000 \text{ hp} = f_3(z)$.
3. Choose total scale length.
4. Find scale factors m_1 and m_2 from $\Delta x = m_1 \Delta f_1$ and $\Delta y = m_2 \Delta f_2$.
5. Find m_3 from m_1 and m_2.
6. Find end points on scale for horsepower.
7. Plot.

CHAPTER FOUR

Statistics in Engineering

4.1 INTRODUCTION

In this chapter we will introduce a subject of increasing importance in engineering design. Mathematical statistics and probability theory have been ignored until recently in engineering curricula. Engineering design in the past often accounted for the inevitable variation of parameters from their design values by introducing "safety factors". Often these safety factors consisted of arbitrarily doubling those dimensions deemed critical in a design. This over-design obtained reliability only at the expense of weight, size, and complexity, which also tended to increase cost. As performance requirements were increased, this intuitive approach began to fail in many engineering design areas. Excess weight became as intolerable to civil engineers designing modern suspension bridges as it did to aircraft designers. Engineers came also to realize that increased complexity did not necessarily improve reliability. It was found that electronic gear, for example, became less reliable as it increased in complexity. Increased complexity means higher performance capability but also more elements that can fail. It has been reported that during the Korean War over one half the radios and other electronic gear of the U.S. Armed Forces were not working at any given moment.

Reliability engineering and *value engineering* are specialties that have been recently created to help cope with this problem. This newer design philosophy is in reality as old as "the one-horse shay." The object is to examine each element in a design and to set its parameters so that all elements are stressed equally. To accomplish this task requires the use of probability and statistics.

Another important application of simple statistical concepts and the elements of probability theory is in designing and interpreting engineering experiments. All too often the beginning engineer finds that he has not the slightest idea of how properly to design an experiment and what information he can reasonably require of the experiment. The design of an experiment is perhaps even more important than the execution of it. The practicing engineer can get help from laboratory technicians and test engineers in the actual hookup and data gathering, but he is solely responsible for the design of the experiment and for the final interpretation of the test results. H. D. Young[1] has written an interesting book on statistics for beginning students in science and engineering. You will be well advised to read the book following this introduction.

4.2 STATISTICS AND PROBABILITY DEFINED

H. Cramér[2] in his classic introduction to probability theory points out that in the middle of the seventeenth century French society was much taken up by gambling. For this reason, considerable attention was focused on developing a theory on games of chance. Notable among the scientists and mathematicians whose interest was caught were Blaise Pascal and Pierre Fermat. The theory built up was that of discrete probability. This involves the chances or expectation of one particular

---

[1] H. D. Young, *Statistical Treatment of Experimental Data* (New York: McGraw-Hill Book Company, Inc., 1962).
[2] H. Cramér, *The Elements of Probability Theory* (New York: John Wiley & Sons, Inc., 1955).

event occurring out of a finite number of possible events. We say, for instance, that the probability of heads turning up when a coin is flipped is one half. Unfortunately, in all but the simplest cases such probabilities, although simple in theory, are difficult to compute.[3]

The more modern approach to probability theory does not retain the ratio of successful outcomes to all possible outcomes as a basic definition of probability. Modern theory emphasizes the stability properties of frequency ratios by saying in effect, in the long run any event will tend to occur with a relative frequency approximately equal to the probability of the event. You may not see any difference between saying that there are six faces on a die and therefore the five spot will turn up with a probability of one sixth on any one roll, and saying that in the long run if the die is rolled many times the five spot will turn up one sixth of the time. But this concept of frequency ratios has in effect extended the meaning of probability theory from a rather specialized rich man's pastime to a central position for all of modern science. It would be rather difficult, for example, to use the original concept of counting sides on a die to compute mortality tables for insurance companies. Yet the frequency ratio concept applies directly.

Statistics are the data gathered on the frequency of occurrence of various events. Statistics are the raw material required for the calculation of probabilities. In accordance with the empirical propositions concerning the long-run stability of frequency ratios, we may expect that for large values of n the observed frequency ratio f/n, where f is the number of successes and n is the number of total trials, will be approximately equal to the probability P of a success on any particular try.

4.3 PROPERTIES OF PROBABILITIES

Consider an experiment in which the event A occurs with a frequency f in the total number of trials n. Then at least we know

$$0 \leq \frac{f}{n} \leq 1$$

---

[3] Evidence of this is given by H. C. Levinson, *Chance, Luck and Statistics* (New York: Dover Publications, Inc., 1963). Levinson points out that more than half of the odds on poker given by Hoyle were wrong, that while the 11th edition of the *Encyclopedia Britannica* improved matters, it still contained a significant number of errors and that even the latest *Britannica* is not totally free of error on this point.

and for large values of n we assume that f/n approximately equals the true probability of the event A occurring on any particular try. Thus,

$$\frac{f}{n}\bigg| \to P(A)$$

$$n \to \infty$$

and

$$0 \le P(A) \le 1 \tag{4.1}$$

The probability of an impossible event is zero and that of a certain event is unity.

Addition Rule

Let A and B denote two events, each of which may or may not occur in a given experiment. The *composed event,* which consists of the occur-

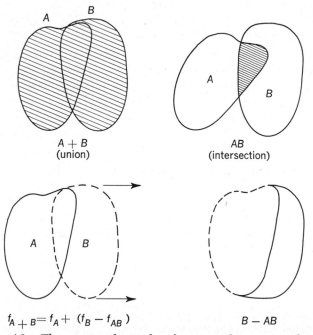

$$A + B$$
(union)

$$AB$$
(intersection)

$$f_{A + B} = f_A + (f_B - f_{AB})$$

$$B - AB$$

Figure 4.1.   The concept of a product from a set theory point of view.

rence of either A or B (or both) in a given experiment, will be called the *sum* and will be designated $A + B$. The occurrence of both A and B in a given experiment will be called the *product* of A and B and will be denoted AB. Now let us perform a series of n repetitions of the experiment, and let f_A, f_B, f_{A+B}, and f_{AB} denote the number of occurrences of A, B, $A + B$, and AB respectively. The following identity will hold because of the basic definition.

$$f_{A+B} = f_A + f_B - f_{AB}$$

For those who had the "new mathematics" in high school, Figure 4.1 presents this idea from a set point of view. Now divide through by n, and assume n large. Then we will have

$$P(A + B) = P(A) + P(B) - P(AB) \qquad (4.2)$$

This is called the addition rule in probability theory.

EXAMPLE 4.1

One card is drawn from each of two decks of 52 cards. What is the probability that at least one of the two cards will be an ace of spades? Call A the event that the card drawn from the first deck is an ace of spades. Call B the event that the second card is an ace of spades. Then obviously, $P(A) = P(B) = 1/52$. Now find $P(AB)$. There are $(52)^2$ possible combinations of drawing one card from the first deck and one from the second. We are interested in only one of these; the event that both cards are aces of spades. Thus $P(AB) = 1/(52)^2$, and Equation (4.2) yields

$$P(A + B) = \frac{1}{52} + \frac{1}{52} - \frac{1}{(52)^2} = \frac{103}{2704}$$

Suppose two events A and B are *mutually exclusive*. That is, if A occurs, then B cannot occur and vice versa. Then $P(AB) = 0$, and Equation (4.2) reduces to the special case

$$P(A + B) = P(A) + P(B) \qquad (4.3)$$

EXAMPLE 4.2

Two cards are simultaneously drawn from the same deck. What is the probability that at least one of them is the ace of spades? Quite obviously they both cannot be the ace of spades; thus, $P(AB) = 0$, and Equation (4.3) applies. After some argument you will agree that $P(A) = P(B) = 1/52$. Thus

$$P(A + B) = \frac{1}{52} + \frac{1}{52} = \frac{1}{26}$$

which may or may not agree with your intuition.

Conditional Probabilities

We wish to define the meaning of just one more symbol. The product or joint probability of two events has been explained, but a somewhat different probability involving two events also turns out to be important. The conditional probability $P(B|A)$ is defined as the probability of B occurring provided, or conditioned on, that A also has occurred. By the familiar concept of frequency ratios, $P(B|A)$ may be found to be

$$P(B|A) = \frac{P(AB)}{P(A)}. \tag{4.4}$$

Equation (4.4) arises in the following way. Consider n repetitions of a given experiment. Suppose event A occurs f_A times. Within this subgroup event B occurs f_{AB} times because within the n experiments there are precisely f_{AB} times that both events occurred, by definition. Thus the ratio f_{AB}/f_A is the frequency ratio of B provided A has also occurred relative to the hypothesis that A has occurred. For large n the respective frequency ratios are the probabilities, and thus we have Equation (4.4).

In exactly the same way we may obtain

$$P(A|B) = \frac{P(AB)}{P(B)} \tag{4.5}$$

Thus $\qquad P(AB) = P(A)P(B|A) = P(B)P(A|B) \tag{4.6}$

Equation (4.6) is called the *multiplier rule*.

EXAMPLE 4.3

Suppose two cards are simultaneously drawn from a deck. What is the probability that they are both spades? Let A be the event that the first card is a spade; let B be the event that the second card is a spade. The equation is $P(A) = 13/52$. If A occurs on the first draw, then the second draw will be from a deck of 51 cards, 12 of which are spades. Thus $P(B|A) = 12/51$. The probability that both cards will be spades follows from Equation (4.4).

$$P(AB) = P(B|A)P(A) = \frac{12}{51} \times \frac{13}{52} = \frac{1}{17}$$

Equation (4.4) can be extended to any number of conditional events.

Independent Events

Suppose now that the conditional probability $P(A|B)$ is the same as the probability of A alone. This indicates that A is *independent* of B. Now if either

$$P(A|B) = P(A) \tag{4.7}$$

or

$$P(B|A) = P(B) \tag{4.8}$$

then the other follows immediately. Moreover, Equation (4.6) then indicates that

$$P(AB) = P(A)P(B) \tag{4.9}$$

This particularly simple special case of the multiplier rule indicates that if events A and B are independent, these two independent probabilities when multiplied yield the joint probability.

Perhaps you are asking about the logical consistency of discussing the probability of event A, supposing that B has occurred, while at the same time considering event A independently of B as in Equations (4.7) and (4.8). A heuristic demonstration of a situation where this occurs may clarify matters. Consider two people who are flipping coins simultaneously. Call this one trial, and take n trials. Let

$A =$ the event that the first coin is heads
$B =$ the event that the second coin is heads
then $AB =$ the event that both coins are heads

Consider the number of times that the event A occurs in n trials a success. This is f_A/n. Now consider a subset of the total n trials, specifically, only those trials in which B occurs. Let us count the number of times A

occurs within this subset. We call this number f_{AB}, since B always occurs in the subset under consideration. The ratio of successes to total trials within this subset is f_{AB}/f_B. Is it not apparent that the ratio of successes in the first instance f_A/n, is the same as it is in the second instance f_{AB}/f_B? That is,

$$\frac{f_A}{n} = \frac{f_{AB}}{f_B}$$

but

$$P(A) = \frac{f_A}{n} = \frac{f_{AB}/n}{f_B/n} = \frac{P(AB)}{P(B)}$$

Now two things become clear. First, the term on the right is defined as $P(A|B)$, and, second, if this result is substituted for $P(A|B)$ in (4.6) we have arrived at Equation (4.9) by an alternate route. It should be clear that the result obtained by the first coin flipper does not depend on what the second flipper does. That is, events A and B are independent. This was our assumption in the original derivation of Equation (4.9).

EXAMPLE 4.4

Suppose a space vehicle designed for photo-reconnaissance of the moon has ten major subsystems, each of which is essential to the successful completion of the mission. If it may be assumed that the reliability of each subsystem is 0.9, what is the probability of a successful mission? We will assume that the probability of successful operation is independent of the other subsystems. The overall probability of success is computed using Equation (4.9).

$$P(\text{success}) = (0.9)^{10} = 0.347 = 0.35$$

or approximately 1 chance in 3 of success.

Suppose by careful engineering the reliability of each component is raised to 0.95 but that to be realistic we consider 100 critical components on which success depends. Then

$$P(\text{success}) = (0.95)^{100} = 0.006$$

or about 1 chance in 200 of success. These simple calculations should show why extreme reliability of each element plus fail-safe capacity and redundancy must be designed into spacecraft.

4.4   THE BINOMIAL DISTRIBUTION

The modern definition of probability is based on the assumed stability of frequency ratios. One of the simplest frequency ratios is that in which the outcome of each repetition of the experiment can consist only of one of two possible alternatives. This situation, although simple in concept, is important, for example, in sampling practice and production quality control.

Sampling is involved whenever the total population under consideration is too large for each individual to be tested, and a sample must be chosen to represent the entire population. As a concrete example of sampling, and therefore of the binomial distribution, consider an urn filled with N balls identical except in color. A proportion $p = f/N$ of the balls are red, and the remainder $(1 - p)$ are white. If one ball is drawn at random from the urn, examined, and replaced, the probability $P(r)$ of its being red is p. A second ball drawn, examined, and replaced would have the same probability of being red. We suppose, of course, that the samples are independent. Apparently there are three possibilities in a draw of two balls.

Both red	$P(r) = (p \times p) = p^2$
One red and one white	$P(rw) = 2p(1 - p)$
Both white	$P(w) = (1 - p)^2$

This argument can be extended to samples of n individuals drawn and replaced from the total population N. The probability of r red balls in a sample of n is

$$P_n{}^r = \frac{n!p^r(1 - p)^{n-r}}{r!(n - r)!} \tag{4.10}$$

EXAMPLE 4.5

Calculate the expected distribution of heads and tails if a coin is flipped 10 times. Apparently here $N = \infty$, $n = 10$, and $p = (1 - p) = 0.5$. For this special case, Equation (4.10) reduces to

$$P_{10}{}^r = \frac{10!(0.5)^{10}}{r!(10 - r)!} = \frac{3.545 \times 10^3}{r!(10 - r)!} \tag{4.11}$$

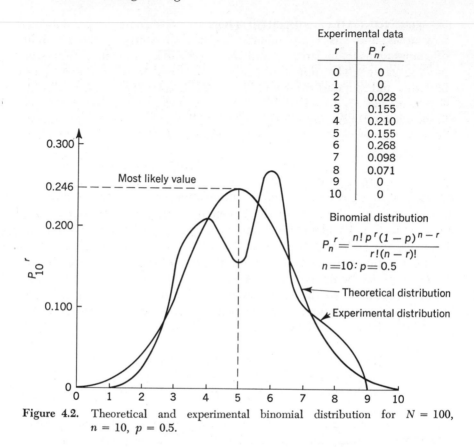

Experimental data

r	$P_n{}^r$
0	0
1	0
2	0.028
3	0.155
4	0.210
5	0.155
6	0.268
7	0.098
8	0.071
9	0
10	0

Binomial distribution

$$P_n{}^r = \frac{n!\,p^r(1-p)^{n-r}}{r!(n-r)!}$$

$$n = 10 : p = 0.5$$

Theoretical distribution

Experimental distribution

Most likely value

Figure 4.2. Theoretical and experimental binomial distribution for $N = 100$, $n = 10$, $p = 0.5$.

Figure 4.2 shows the plot along with experimentally determined data for the same conditions. Note that the average value or expected value is 5 heads out of 10, but also notice that this most likely number is really not very probable. The data in Figure 4.2 are connected by a smooth curve to show the form of the distribution, but you will realize that this is not really correct. The distribution is only defined at the integers. Thus, we should only show spikes at the whole numbers.

Prediction of Sample Distribution

From 1960 to 1964, compact and sports car sales held steady at approximately 40 percent of the total United States' new car market.[4] A corporation involved in the aerospace business is interested in expanding into new areas, and has a preliminary design team studying the feasibility of manufacturing in large quantities a standard, automatic, multi-story parking garage. The unit would be manufactured in the present aircraft factories and shipped disassembled to the permanent location. The design team has predicted that within the next decade municipalities will force wholesale construction of such units by use of their taxing powers in order to arrest the decay of the urban core. Thus, the team places a premium on ground space occupied by the unit. Assuming the figures in the *Fortune* study will remain approximately constant in the foreseeable future, how many compact-car places would you allocate in a 100-car garage?

We will assume that a space built for a standard-size automobile

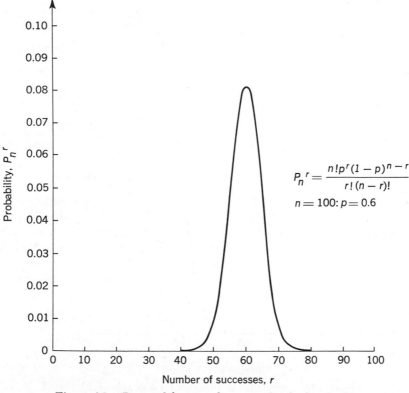

$$P_n^{\,r} = \frac{n!\,p^r(1-p)^{n-r}}{r!\,(n-r)!}$$

$$n = 100 : p = 0.6$$

Figure 4.3.   Binomial function for a sample of a hundred.

can equally well accept a compact car but not the converse Let *p* be the relative number of standard cars in the normal population. In Figure 4.3 is plotted the binomial distribution for $n = 100$ and $p = 0.6$. It is apparent that to provide 40 compact spaces, merely because this is the expected number of compacts in a normal sample, will cost the garage operator business. In fact, on this basis, on one-half of his operating days he will be turning away standard-size cars while he still has spaces for compact cars remaining empty.

Suppose it is decided that a 1 in 10 chance of having to turn away a standard car while there is still an empty compact space is a reasonable design compromise. Then, rather than concerning ourselves with the specific probability of a given ratio of standard cars to the total number of customers on a given day such as $P(60/100)$ occurring, we wish

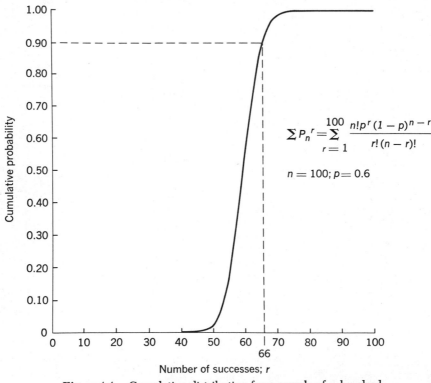

$$\sum P_n{}^r = \sum_{r=1}^{100} \frac{n! p^r (1 - p)^{n-r}}{r! (n - r)!}$$

$$n = 100; p = 0.6$$

Figure 4.4. Cumulative distribution for a sample of a hundred.

to add up the probabilities of all possible ratios until the sum of these probabilities equals 0.9.

$$P(\text{design}) = P(0/100) + P(1/100) + \cdots P(r/100) = 0.9 \qquad (4.12)$$

The number r that gives the summed probabilities the value 0.9 is the number we seek. The concept of summing (that is, integrating) all probabilities up to and including a certain value is called a *cumulative distribution*. Figure 4.4 shows the cumulative distribution for this specific example. Naturally there are far better ways than this to compute cumulative probabilities.[5] By examining Figure 4.4, it is apparent that 90 percent of the samples will be acceptable if 34 compact spaces are provided.

Note in this example that engineering judgment is essential in the application of statistics. You might ask yourself, for example, if special provision should be made for parking units located in California where sports cars abound or near college campuses where Volkswagens are numerous.

Testing Hypotheses

Suppose you are a prospective purchaser of an automatic garage such as we have been discussing. A salesman for the manufacturer has given you a lecture on how scientifically the unit has been designed. Your first inclination perhaps will be to doubt such a complicated sales pitch. Your second inclination might be to go to the location you have been thinking about for the garage and to count the number of sport/compact cars in the first 100 cars that go by. In effect, you are testing the hypothesis given by *Fortune* and which was used in the design. If 99 out of the first 100 cars were sport/compacts, you would have a right to doubt the hypothesis. On the other hand, a particular ratio, even the most probable, is not very likely. We see from Figure 4.3 that 60 standard-size cars out of a random sample of 100 will occur only with a probability of 0.0812, even though this is the expected value. How then can we test the design hypothesis against some other proposed or alternative hypothesis? This is a somewhat complex matter and really beyond the level of detail we have chosen for this text.

[5] For an interesting discussion of this problem see F. Mosteller, R. E. K. Rourke, and G. B. Thomas, Jr., *Probability with Statistical Applications* (Reading, Mass.: Addison-Wesley Publishing Company, Inc., 1961), Chapt. 7.

Estimation

Probably the prospective purchaser of the automatic garage would not be really interested in what is technically called "testing a hypothesis," in the sense of comparing it with one other possibility. In the parking garage example surely there is *some* number which represents the ratio under consideration.

Hypothesis testing is valuable in deciding between several possible outcomes once the alternatives have been narrowed down. Is this fertilizer better than that one? Does Purdue have a better basketball team this year than Ohio State? Is this drug useful or harmful in arresting the symptoms of cancer? Our prospective garage purchaser wants to know the answer to the more general question: What is the ratio of compact cars to standard passing this particular corner?[6] Note that the answer to this more general question contains within it the answer to the more restricted one of hypothesis testing. Interestingly enough, the more general question is easier to answer.[7]

The process of estimation involves the concept of a *confidence interval*. Equation (4.10) permits a direct calculation of the probability of drawing a random sample with a ratio r/n given p. Consequently, it can be used to plot a three-dimensional diagram in which the probability of r out of n for fixed n is a function of both r and p. Figure 4.5 is based on $n = 100$. Suppose we were to mark off a contour line around this ridge which includes within it a given fraction of the total volume of the ridge. There would be various possibilities for placing this contour, but we will draw it symmetrically on each side of the ridge. If the contour surrounds 95 percent of the total volume, there will be only a 5-percent chance, 1 in 20, of a particular test falling outside the contour. Any other contour can also be marked off. These contours are called confidence limits, and the area enclosed on the *p-r* plane is called the confidence interval. Table 4.1 has been constructed to show a 95 percent confidence level. Note that as the sample size is increased, the limits narrow in on the expected value. For example, if our customer

---

[6] Really we should add ". . . that are customers," but this would require a careful and expensive market survey. We also should add "over the lifetime of the garage," but this requires prediction. You should be alert to all the assumptions implicit in a proposal.

[7] This surprising situation occurs regularly in science and has been given the name *invariant imbedding* by the mathematician Richard Bellman, whose *dynamic programming* is a more complex example of the same phenomenon.

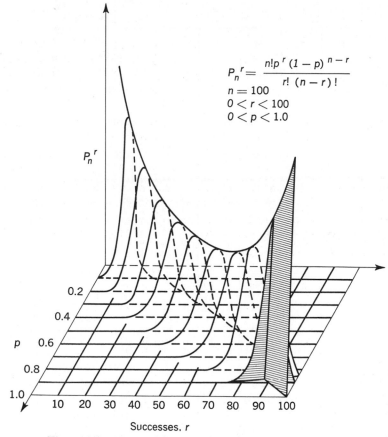

$$P_n^{\ r} = \frac{n!p^{\,r}(1-p)^{\,n-r}}{r!\,(n-r)!}$$
$$n = 100$$
$$0 < r < 100$$
$$0 < p < 1.0$$

Figure 4.5.   Binomial function for a sample of a hundred.

actually observed 40 percent of the sport/compact cars, he would be 95 percent sure that the proper ratio lies between 30 percent and 50 percent if he observed a total of $n = 100$. If $n = 250$, the limits narrow to 34 percent and 45 percent, and with $n = 1000$ the range is 37 percent to 43 percent. To increase the confidence level to 99 percent would broaden the limits in all cases.

Paired Comparison

Another application of the binomial distribution which we will not go into here is the testing of hypotheses by comparing a series of test cases each with its control pair. Tables are available for this so-called

Table 4.1 Ninety-five Percent Confidence Intervals (percent) for Binomial Distribution*

NUMBER OBSERVED r	SIZE OF SAMPLE n 10		15		20		30		50		100		FRACTION OBSERVED r/n	SIZE OF SAMPLE 250		1000	
0	0	31	0	22	0	17	0	12	0	7	0	4	0.00	0	1	0	0
1	0	45	0	32	0	25	0	17	0	11	0	5	0.01	0	4	0	2
2	3	56	2	40	1	31	1	22	0	14	0	7	0.02	1	5	1	3
3	7	65	4	48	3	38	2	27	1	17	1	8	0.03	1	6	2	4
4	12	74	8	55	6	44	4	31	2	19	1	10	0.04	2	7	3	5
5	19	81	12	62	9	49	6	35	3	22	2	11	0.05	3	9	4	7
6	26	88	16	68	12	54	8	39	5	24	2	12	0.06	3	10	5	8
7	35	93	21	73	15	59	10	43	6	27	3	14	0.07	4	11	6	9
8	44	97	27	79	19	64	12	46	7	29	4	15	0.08	5	12	6	10
9	55	100	32	84	23	68	15	50	9	31	4	16	0.09	6	13	7	11
10	69	100	38	88	27	73	17	53	10	34	5	18	0.10	7	14	8	12
11			45	92	32	77	20	56	12	36	5	19	0.11	7	16	9	13
12			52	96	36	81	23	60	13	38	6	20	0.12	8	17	10	14
13			60	98	41	85	25	63	15	41	7	21	0.13	9	18	11	15
14			68	100	46	88	28	66	16	43	8	22	0.14	10	19	12	16
15			78	100	51	91	31	69	18	44	9	24	0.15	10	20	13	17
16					56	94	34	72	20	46	9	25	0.16	11	21	14	18
17					62	97	37	75	21	48	10	26	0.17	12	22	15	19
18					69	99	40	77	23	50	11	27	0.18	13	23	16	21
19					75	100	44	80	25	53	12	28	0.19	14	24	17	22
20					83	100	47	83	27	55	13	29	0.20	15	26	18	23
21							50	85	28	57	14	30	0.21	16	27	19	24
22							54	88	30	59	14	31	0.22	17	28	19	25
23							57	90	32	61	15	32	0.23	18	29	20	26
24							61	92	34	63	16	33	0.24	19	30	21	27
25							65	94	36	64	17	35	0.25	20	31	22	28
26							69	96	37	66	18	36	0.26	20	32	23	29
27							73	98	39	68	19	37	0.27	21	33	24	30
28							78	99	41	70	19	38	0.28	22	34	25	31
29							83	100	43	72	20	39	0.29	23	35	26	32
30							88	100	45	73	21	40	0.30	24	36	27	33
31									47	75	22	41	0.31	25	37	28	34
32									50	77	23	42	0.32	26	38	29	35
33									52	79	24	43	0.33	27	39	30	36
34									54	80	25	44	0.34	28	40	31	37
35									56	82	26	45	0.35	29	41	32	38
36									57	84	27	46	0.36	30	42	33	39
37									59	85	28	47	0.37	31	43	34	40
38									62	87	28	48	0.38	32	44	35	41
39									64	88	29	49	0.39	33	45	36	42
40									66	90	30	50	0.40	34	46	37	43
41									69	91	31	51	0.41	35	47	38	44
42									71	93	32	52	0.42	36	48	39	43
43									73	94	33	53	0.43	37	49	40	46
44									76	95	34	54	0.44	38	50	41	47
45									78	97	35	55	0.45	39	51	42	48
46									81	98	36	56	0.46	40	52	43	49
47									83	99	37	57	0.47	41	53	44	50
48									86	100	38	58	0.48	42	54	45	51
49									89	100	39	59	0.49	43	55	46	52
50									93	100	40	60	0.50	44	56	47	53
												†		‡‡		‡‡	

* Reprinted by permission from G. W. Snedecor, *Statistical Methods*, © 1956 by the Iowa State Press, Ames, Iowa.

† If r exceeds 50, read 100 − r = number observed, and subtract each confidence limit from 100.

‡‡ If r/n exceeds 0.50, read 1.00 − r/n = fraction observed, and subtract each confidence limit from 100.

sign test in which the number of times the test must succeed is compared to its pair for the hypothesis to succeed. For further details see E. B. Wilson.[8]

4.5   THE NORMAL DISTRIBUTION

In many sampling problems it is impossible to assume that the population consists of only two classes. There may be a spread or distribution of values. The population under consideration might be the grades in an examination or the height, or weight, or age of a certain group of people, or the lifetime of a certain group of light bulbs and so on. A number of distribution functions have been proposed for various situations but the only one, besides the binomial, that we will study is the normal distribution. The normal or Gaussian distribution is the most common of all the distributions and, in fact, may be considered the most general.

Karl Friedrich Gauss (1777–1855), commonly included with Archimedes and Newton as one of the three great mathematical minds of the ages, applied himself to the question of errors involved in astronomical observations. After taking the best value as the arithmetic mean of the observations and adding a further assumption about a meaningful criterion of precision, he showed that this necessitated a normal distribution of errors of estimation. Generally speaking, however, the Gaussian or normal distribution is a heuristic assumption made in the absence of evidence to the contrary.

The normal distribution is defined by

$$P(x) = \frac{1}{\sqrt{2\pi\sigma^2}} e^{-(x-\mu)^2/2\sigma^2} \qquad (4.13)$$

where $\mu \triangleq$ the mean or expected (most likely) value of the probability
$\sigma \triangleq$ standard deviation, a measure of the spread of the distribution
$\sigma^2 \triangleq$ variance
$e \triangleq$ the transcendental number 2.718281828459045235360287 . . .

A plot of Equation (4.13) for $\mu = 1$ and two values of σ is shown in Figure 4.6.

[8] E. B. Wilson, Jr., *An Introduction to Scientific Research* (New York: McGraw-Hill Book Company, Inc., 1952), Chapt. 8.

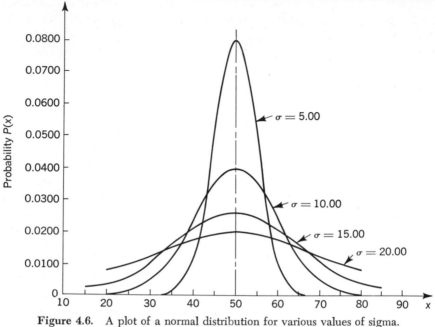

Figure 4.6.   A plot of a normal distribution for various values of sigma.

The binomial distribution is *discrete* and is defined only at the integers. The normal distribution is *continuous* and is defined at all points. We can calculate a value for $P(x)$ given any x. We are tempted to say that a point on the curve represents the probability of the event x occurring. This cannot be correct, however, since the probability of any specific number out of the infinity of numbers between any two points must be zero. Rather, we must interpret it as follows. (See Figure 4.7.) Given a value x_0 and a small distance Δx centered on it, the area $P(x_0) \, \Delta x$ is the probability of an event occurring in the range Δx. The tiny area $P(x_0) \, \Delta x$ then represents the probability rather than a line or a point on the curve. All the tiny areas under the curve add up to unity.

You will have no difficulty in applying the concept of confidence intervals we have already developed to the normal distribution for a given value of σ and an assumed value for μ. You will find once again that by choosing the confidence limits symmetrically about the expected value, they can enclose the greatest area for a given spacing. For this

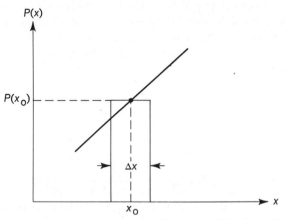

Figure 4.7.   The area of the rectangle of width ΔX and height $P(X_0)$ is the probability of an event occurring within the tiny range ΔX.

condition Table 4.2 gives the spacing for a given confidence level in terms of σ.

Table 4.2   Confidence Intervals for the Normal Distribution*   (Confidence levels are centered about μ for a given value of σ.)

CONFIDENCE LEVEL	CONFIDENCE INTERVALS
0.50	$\mu \pm 0.674\sigma$
0.80	$\mu \pm 1.282\sigma$
0.90	$\mu \pm 1.645\sigma$
0.95	$\mu \pm 1.960\sigma$
0.99	$\mu \pm 2.576\sigma$
0.999	$\mu \pm 3.291\sigma$

* From Wilson, p. 237 (see footnote 8).

For a given standard deviation σ it is almost a 20 to 1 bet that all observations will fall within two standard deviations of the actual mean value or expected value. This is a very commonly used spread.

Suppose now that it is assumed that a number of observations have been made of a normal population, the observations have been averaged and the mean value $\bar{x}$ is found. It turns out to be possible[9] to find how to relate this value to μ, the true mean value of the total population in terms of the number of samples n and the confidence limits. For 95 percent confidence

$$\bar{x} - \frac{1.96\sigma}{\sqrt{n}} < \mu < \bar{x} + \frac{1.96\sigma}{\sqrt{n}} \qquad (4.14)$$

where σ is assumed known. For any other confidence limits the appropriate values from Table 4.2 may be substituted in Equation (4.14). It should be mentioned that Equation (4.14) assumes that each observation is independent and that the disturbances which cause each reading to differ are random. We note from Equation (4.14) that taking n observations closes down the confidence interval by $\sqrt{n}$.

EXAMPLE 4.6

We wish to obtain the mean value of a certain Gaussian process with a fixed μ and a given σ of 1.0. From a single sample function it appears that the measured value for the mean is $\bar{x} = 5$. With a confidence level of 95 percent, what is the actual mean value of the process? By the use of Table 4.2 and Equation (4.14) we determine that

$$3.04 \leq \mu \leq 6.96$$

This is not very satisfactory, of course. There is more than a 2 to 1 ratio between the two limits. Suppose the confidence limits must be brought closer. If an average of four readings is taken, then by Equation (4.14)

$$4.02 \leq \mu \leq 5.98$$

This is better but still not very good. To cut the tolerance in half again requires sixteen readings. Then

$$4.51 \leq \mu \leq 5.49$$

This is still not spectacular precision.

Perhaps this is the place to dispel the myth of "the best two out of three." For some reason all red-blooded American boys, when faced with a laboratory measurement, take three readings. Usually two of the three are close together, with the third somewhat off. The tendency is arbitrarily to throw out the third reading and average the remaining two. We now can see the error in this procedure.

[9] Wilson, p. 238 (see footnote 8).

Often the standard deviation of an assumed normal population is un-known. Even here the confidence limits are reduced by $\sqrt{n}$, and some-what more advanced techniques involving *students t-distribution* will yield numerical results.[10] Remember that repeated observations (so-called replication) reduced the spread caused by random errors but have no effect on *systematic* errors. Examples of systematic errors are reading the wrong scale, bias in the measuring equipment, and an operator's bias. An example of an operator's bias occurs whenever an experimenter starts out with a desire to prove (or disprove) a theory.

The *probable error* of an observation is defined as that range about the expected value which will include one half the total population of read-ings. If the population is normal, we see from Table 4.2 that

$$\text{Probable error} = 0.674\sigma$$

Whether the observer chooses to report probable error, confidence limits, or the standard deviation, it is *essential* that some measure of precision be given.

4.6   QUALITY CONTROL

In 1931 W. A. Shewhart[11] reduced to text form a new body of theory that has grown into an important portion of the field of industrial engi-neering. Quality control is of basic importance to the control of mass production processes, and, as Wilson[12] points out in his excellent intro-duction, more recently the theory has been applied to detection of exper-imental errors of a wide variety of types. We will not develop the theory of quality control here beyond a few elementary principles.

Suppose an experiment has been set up and a series of observations made on a presumably constant parameter, or suppose a production line has been designed to produce items that will remain within rigid tolerances. In both cases, when the actual values are measured, there will be variations about the design center. The question to be answered by the engineer in charge is whether the measured value is in control. The phrase *in control* means that no steady drift or *trend* exists, and

[10] Wilson, p. 239 (see footnote 8). See also Section 4.6 of this chapter.
[11] W. A. Shewhart, *Economic Control of Quality of Manufactured Products* (Princeton, N.J.: D. Van Nostrand Company, Inc., 1931).
[12] Wilson, pp. 258–272 (see footnote 8).

that *jumps* and *periodic variations* are absent. In other words, that the variation about the design center is random and within desired limits. The simplest means of insuring this is to record and examine the observed data for statistical significance.

Quality Control Charts

Suppose it is assumed that the variation of an observed quantity about some mean value is caused by random disturbances with a Gaussian distribution. Then from our previous discussion (see Table 4.2) it is apparent that 95 percent of the reading will lie within $\pm 1.960\sigma$, or approximately $\pm 2\sigma$, and 99.7 percent will lie within $\pm 3\sigma$ of the mean. The $\pm 3\sigma$ limits are usually employed in quality control charts.

A quality control chart is produced in the following way. First, a number of single observations are gathered together in equal-sized groups, and the mean of each group is computed. The grouping must not rearrange the chronological order of the observations, but the size depends on the individual requirements. Each group may consist of thousands of observations taken for a whole day, or, on the other hand, each group may have only three or four elements. The mean of each group is plotted versus an index (such as number of days) as shown in Figure 4.8. Second, the mean of all of the measurements is computed and plotted as a solid line. Finally, σ is computed, and the $\pm 3\sigma$ lines are plotted as dashed lines. If any point falls outside the 3σ lines, the experiment is said to go out of control at that point. Note that a significant amount of data must be amassed before a quality control chart can be constructed.

One further point intrudes. In previous work we have assumed that σ is known. Now it must be computed. It turns out that the computation on the variance σ^2 or the standard deviation σ of a finite amount of experimental data is a problem of major concern to statisticians. The student t-distribution, for example, was designed to aid in this purpose. We will use a relation for the *sample standard deviation s,* which is derived in most texts on statistics.

$$s = \left[\frac{\sum_{i=1}^{n} (x_i - \bar{x})^2}{n-1} \right]^{1/2} \tag{4.15}$$

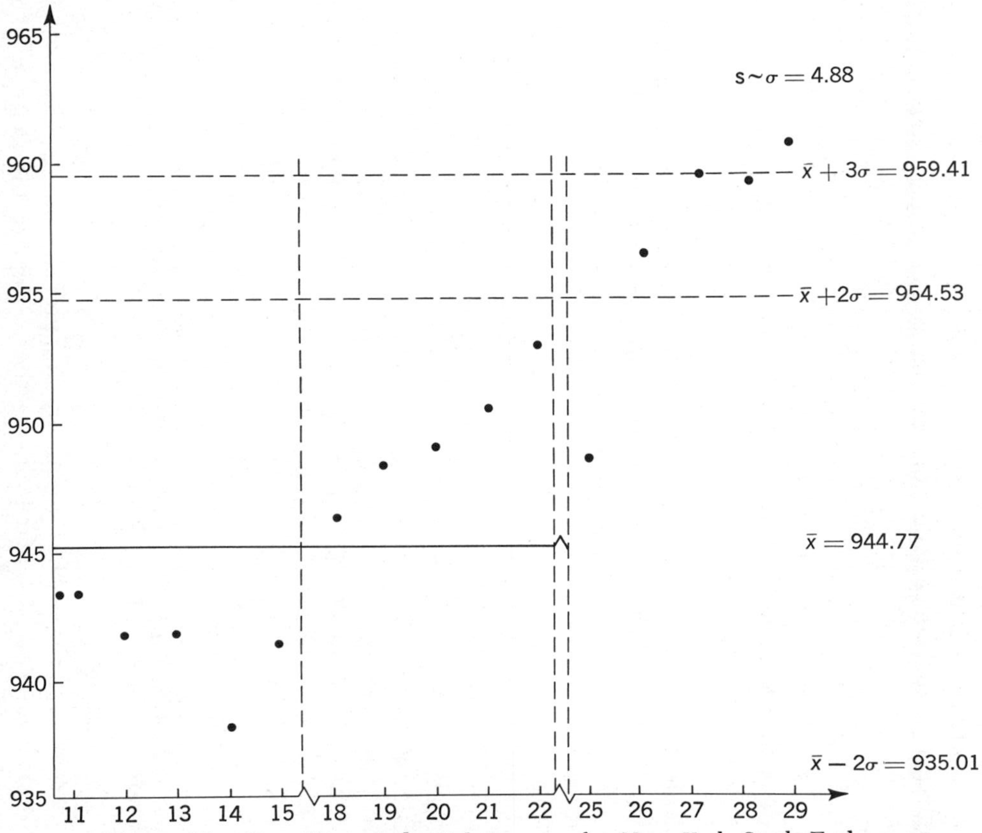

Date 1966	Dow Jones Industrial Average
Oct. 11	942.65
12	941.12
13	941.01
14	937.50
15	940.68
18	945.84
19	947.76
20	948.47
21	950.28
22	952.42
25	948.14
26	956.32
27	959.50
28	959.11
29	960.82
Nov. 1	958.96
2	closed
3	961.13
4	961.85
5	959.46

$s \sim \sigma = 4.88$

$\bar{x} + 3\sigma = 959.41$

$\bar{x} + 2\sigma = 954.53$

$\bar{x} = 944.77$

$\bar{x} - 2\sigma = 935.01$

Figure 4.8. Dow Jones Industrial Average for New York Stock Exchange over a two-week period.

89

where $s \triangleq$ sample standard deviation
$\quad \bar{x} \triangleq$ sample mean
$\quad n \triangleq$ number of observations
$\quad x_i \triangleq$ value of ith observation

We use symbols s and $\bar{x}$ here rather than σ and μ to emphasize that these are approximations of the true values, calculated with perhaps only a few observations. Naturally, we expect the value of s and $\bar{x}$ to approach the exact values for σ and μ as the number of observations becomes large.

Use of the student t-distribution and s results in a somewhat different relation for confidence limits from the one we used when σ was known,

$$\bar{x} - \frac{k}{n} s < \mu < \bar{x} + \frac{k}{n} s \qquad (4.16)$$

where the parameter k is given in Table 4.3.

Table 4.3.   Values of the Parameter k for Confidence-limit Calculation Using the Sample Standard Deviation s*

NUMBER OF OBSERVATIONS IN GROUP		CONFIDENCE LEVEL			
n	0.50	0.80	0.90	0.95	0.99
2	1.00	3.08	6.31	12.71	63.66
3	0.82	1.89	2.92	4.30	9.93
4	0.77	1.64	2.35	3.18	5.84
5	0.74	1.53	2.13	2.78	4.60
6	0.73	1.48	2.02	2.57	4.03
∞	0.67	1.28	1.65	1.96	2.58

* Abridged from Table IV of Fisher & Yates, *Statistical Tables for Biological, Agricultural and Medical Research,* published by Oliver & Boyd Ltd., Edinburgh, and by permission of the authors and publishers.

A somewhat simpler but less accurate approximation for σ from a few observations may be found by using the concept of the *range w*. The range is defined as the difference between the largest and smallest values in a group. E. B. Wilson gives the following relation for confidence intervals using the range w

$$\bar{x} - c_n w < \mu < \bar{x} + c_n w \qquad (4.17)$$

where the coefficient c_n may be found in Table 4.3 for various confidence levels.

Table 4.4   Values of the Parameter c_n for Confidence-Limit Calculation Using the Range w*

NUMBER OF OBSERVATIONS IN GROUP	CONFIDENCE LEVEL			
n	0.90	0.95	0.98	0.99
2	3.20	6.35	15.90	31.83
3	0.88	1.30	2.11	3.01
4	0.53	0.72	1.02	1.32
5	0.39	0.51	0.68	0.84
6	0.31	0.40	0.52	0.63
10	0.19	0.23	0.29	0.33

* From E. Lord, *Biometrica*, **34**, 41, 1947, Table 9.

To return now to the specific problem of calculating the confidence limits for the quality control chart for small-sized subgroups. Wilson gives a convenient calculation. The standard deviation σ may be approximated by

$$\sigma = 1.023\bar{w}, \qquad 3\sigma = 3.070\bar{w} \text{ (groups with three elements)}$$

or

$$\sigma = 0.971\bar{w}, \qquad 3\sigma = 2.914\bar{w} \text{ (groups with four elements)}$$

where $\bar{w}$ is the mean range of the groups.

EXAMPLE 4.7   A QUALITY CONTROL CHART

Suppose we have become interested in the stock market and wish to know if the daily trend is up or down. The Dow-Jones Industrial Index is a well-known indicator of the state of the market. In Figure 4.8 is shown two weeks of data from this index. The mean of these 10 points is 944.77 and is shown as a solid line. Now use Equation (4.15) to compute s, the sample standard deviation.

$$s = \left[\tfrac{1}{9} \sum_{i=1}^{10} (x_i - \bar{x})^2 \right]^{1/2} = \{ \tfrac{1}{9}[(942.65 - 944.77)^2 + \cdots$$

$$+ (952.42 - 944.77)^2]\}^{1/2} \quad (4.18)$$

$$= \sqrt{23.82} = 4.88$$

The $\pm 2s$ and $\pm 3s$ lines are shown dotted. Although the market remains within the $2s$ boundaries, there appears to be an upward trend developing during the week of the 18th. More data should be gathered before definite conclusions can be drawn.[13] If an investor were interested in the relatively long-term movement of the market over the course of the year, it seems natural to gather data values in groups of five. Then a point on the new longer-term scale would represent a week's average value.

PROBLEMS

4.1 If one card is drawn from a deck of 52, what is the probability that it will be either an ace or a spade?

4.2 One card is drawn from each of two decks of 52 cards. What is the probability that at least one of the two cards is a spade?

4.3 There are 23 percent girls in the undergraduate student body of a university. Seventeen percent of the girls are blondes. What is the probability that the first student you meet on campus will be a blonde girl?

4.4 You have drawn two cards from a deck and placed them face up on the table. They are the seven and ace of hearts. What is the probability that the next card drawn from the remainder of the deck will be either an ace or a heart?

4.5 Forty percent of all automobiles on United States highways are reputed to be compact or sports cars. Fifty-five percent of all cars on

---

[13] The data for October 25–29 are plotted without recalculating the mean value and continue to indicate an upward trend. However, the mean and deviation really should be recalculated if the chart is applied sequentially.

the road were manufactured by General Motors (GM). One fifth of GM's production is in compact/sports cars. What is the probability that the next automobile you will see will be a GM sports/compact car?

4.6 Using the data given in Problem 5, what is the probability that the next car you see will be either a GM car or a sports/compact car?

4.7 It has been determined that there is 1 chance in 50 of a hunter being blasted by some other hunter on opening day of the deer season. On all other days the chances are only 1 in 200. What is the probability of a hunter coming through the entire 21-day season unscathed if he hunts every day?

4.8 Let ten tosses of a coin constitute one event. Plot the number of heads in each event for 100 events. Obtain data experimentally, then compute the theoretical distribution and compare the results.

4.9 An experiment consists of tossing a coin eight times. Compute:
   a. The probability of obtaining only one head.
   b. The probability of obtaining only one head and having it occur on the fourth toss.
   c. The probability that two or more heads will be obtained.
   d. The probability that one or more heads will appear but not until after the third toss.

4.10 A certain transistor is designed to have a nominal current gain of $\beta = 50$. However, because of manufacturing uncertainties, a relatively wide dispersion in gains is experienced. Assume that the gains are distributed normally about the average value of $\bar{\beta} = 50$ and that the standard deviation is 20. What percentage of the resistors have gains which lie in the region $40 \leq \beta \leq 100$? *Hint:* Use tables for areas under the normal distribution curve.

4.11 Many other distributions tend toward the normal under certain circumstances. We can use this fact (the so-called central limit theorem) to evaluate the cumulative binomial distribution in the parking garage example in a somewhat less painful way than counting squares.[14]

---

[14] It may interest the historically minded that we follow in this problem precisely the purpose for which Abraham de Moivre originally developed the normal distribution in 1733.

The mean (expected) value of the binomial distribution $\bar{r}$ and the standard deviation σ, are given by

$$\bar{r} = np \qquad \text{and} \qquad \sigma = [np(1-p)]^{\frac{1}{2}}$$

For large n the shape of the binomial distribution approaches that of the normal. Thus we can use the commonly available tables of area under the normal distribution to evaluate the area under the binomial. Usually these tables are constructed for zero mean and unit standard deviation. In order to adjust a binomial index r to a Gaussian index x we write

$$x = \frac{r - \frac{1}{2} - np}{[np(1-p)]^{\frac{1}{2}}}$$

Use this technique and a table of Gaussian distributions to compute the proper number of standard-size car spaces in the parking garage example.

CHAPTER FIVE

Economics in Engineering Design

5.1 INTRODUCTION

It is commonly said that the engineer may be distinguished from the theoretical scientist by his concern for the economics of the projects he undertakes. Doubtless this is an inaccurate statement, but it does contain a grain of truth. Part of the index of performance by which the engineer judges the success of a program is cost or profitability.

Thought of in the narrow sense, money does not seem to have a proper place in matters of life or death. We surely want safe highways, an adequate defense establishment, and an adequate air-traffic control system—independent of the unit cost. On the other hand, critics of the space program argue that it is being conducted in complete disregard of the costs involved. Yet in all these examples, cost is directly involved.

In a broad sense, cost is an excellent index by which to measure performance. For example, suppose two air-traffic control systems are proposed, and both meet the desired performance specifications. Naturally you would pick the less costly of the two simply to save money. However, there are several other excellent reasons for this choice. The cheaper system probably contains fewer and simpler parts, and therefore its reliability should be higher. The cheaper system is no doubt built around certain standard subassemblies that are in production and for which development costs have already been amortized. Use of standard high-production-run subunits also tends to increase reliability and to insure that servicing will be available when needed. Furthermore, if the cost of the unit is less, it usually indicates that manufacturing is simpler, and therefore production and delivery will be quicker. Finally, proper economics applied to the unit cost means that more of the units can be placed in service for the same total cost, thus insuring wider use of the system and consequent benefits. Naturally this discussion assumes that all performance standards are met and that the manufacturer of the cheaper system is reputable, is capable of accurately assessing his own costs, and that he is not taking a loss in order to break into a new line.

It is immoral and unethical for an engineer to encourage a supplier either to overbid in hopes of a quick killing or to underbid in order to break into the field. Economics must be based on sound business practices, and an unusually high or low bid often indicates a lack of knowledge of the field or of extraneous factors being included. Such factors cloud the issue and make objective judgments difficult. Naturally, one must be alert to possible new factors that may make a bid that seems out of line realistic after careful consideration.

To place economic studies in their proper perspective, we list in order the three broad steps of a preliminary engineering design.

(1) Moral, ethical, and legal aspects.
(2) Economic aspects.
(3) Technical aspects.

An engineer cannot and should not try to avoid the consequences of his professional acts. A free citizen in a democracy can never take refuge in excuses such as "Well, everyone else is doing it," or "My boss made me do it." The revulsion of alert citizens at the revelation in 1960 of widespread and long-standing price fixing in the electrical utility industry and the subsequent jail sentences for vice-presidents of several important American manufacturing concerns is a forceful example of this ethical principle.[1]

An engineer should search his conscience before accepting a job in an industry engaged in activities harmful to society. Alexander Maddow, director of a research institute of the Royal Cancer Hospital,[2] gives a particularly horrifying example of such behavior in the British rubber and chemical industry, which has delayed for over 70 years the prohibition of known cancer-inducing materials such as β-naphthylamine, benzidine, 4-aminobiphenyl, and 4-nitrobiphenyl used as antioxidants during the manufacture of rubber. There have been over 600 cases in England and Wales of occupationally related bladder cancer, a number of which have been terminal. Most of these were discovered long after the causal relation was well established. The tobacco business today is probably another example of such disregard for the public welfare.

Legal aspects of a new proposal must also be considered before proceeding with a design. For example, property rights and patent restrictions must be checked. The second step in a feasibility study is economic. What is the expected return on the anticipated investment, and how does this compare with other investment proposals? This is the question that must be answered before detailed technical design is begun. Preliminary design will provide the information required to answer this question.

5.2 ECONOMIC DECISIONS

In this section we will mention a number of types of decisions an engineer could be called on to make that are based on economic factors. The first of these, long-term profitability, is basic to a preliminary design study.

The Long-term Profitability of a New Venture

The judgment to proceed with a new venture is based on a study of the rate of return on invested capital. Any group, whether it be

---

[1] John G. Fuller, *The Gentlemen Conspirators* (New York: Grove Press Inc., 1962).
[2] A. Maddow, "Control of Cancer-Inducing Chemicals," *New Scientist*, No. 430, February 1965, p. 345.

as small as a young married couple or as large as the government of the United States, is faced with capital limitations. There are always more things to be done than money to do them with. This fact is so basic that it is constantly a source of mental fantasy. We like to dream about life with an unlimited supply of money.

Since capital is limited, a corporation must carefully compare various proposed courses of action to find the most profitable. This is not as easy as it first sounds and is ignored even today by administrators of corporations who should know better. One of the lasting contributions of Alfred P. Sloan, former chairman of the board of General Motors, was his concern for cash flow and objective accounting procedures. It is no accident that General Motors is not only the largest corporation in the nation but is consistently one of the most profitable.[3] On the other hand, the Ford Motor Company, which dominated the field in the early days because of the inventive and mechanical genius of Henry Ford, was driven almost to bankruptcy by the 1940s because of his lack of appreciation of cost accounting.

A suitable topic in the study of rate of return on investment is the proposed supersonic transport aircraft or SST. Preliminary studies seem to indicate that the operating cost of a March-3 transport will be 26 percent higher than present jet transports for transcontinental flights. This is due to the unexpected efficiency of present aircraft and consequent lowering of operating costs as well as the higher cost of the SST. A United Airlines' study shows that for "short hauls," such as between Chicago and Los Angeles, the operating cost may be 43 percent higher.[4] This figure assumes, although unrealistically, that terminal operation patterns are similar to today's patterns. According to simulation studies, the number of terminal operations per day must be reduced to provide a safety margin that will raise the cost of each take off and each landing.[5] The cost figures do not include the more or less normal contingencies either. For example, one extra S-shape turn in a transonic climb-out from an airport will require 16,000 lb of extra fuel (*Aviation Week*, October 5, 1964). As a result of these factors, the remark of an Air India official

[3] P. F. Drucker, *The Concept of the Corporation* (New York: Mentor New American Library, 1964).
[4] "SST May Cause Route Competition Curbs," *Aviation Week*, **81**, No. 18, November 2, 1964, p. 30.
[5] "Study Finds SST Will Reduce Terminal Operations," *Aviation Week*, **81**, No. 14, October 5, 1964, p. 29. Also "SST Economics Worry IATA Conferees," *Aviation Week*, **81**, No. 13, September 28, 1964, p. 29.

that "we can't pay five times present costs for two and one half times present productivity" seems to make good sense. As a result of operator opposition to the SST, aircraft manufacturers are reluctant to bear even as little as 10 percent of the development costs,[6] and new subsonic jets will continue to be built.[7] As a result of these careful economic cost studies, which themselves cost thousands of dollars, the national economy will hopefully be spared many millions of dollars of waste in premature "crash" development of an expensive white elephant.[8]

This is not to say, of course, that research and development on the SST should be halted; in fact, quite the contrary. Research and development should continue at an efficient pace, with perhaps a target date for "roll-out" of the first test vehicle by 1975 and production of the aircraft by 1980.

Build or Buy Decisions

Once a venture has been determined to be economically sound, one must choose from among a number of alternative methods of procedure. A basic question is whether to build the device within the company or to purchase it from an outside vendor. For example, suppose your company manufactures aircraft engines. It carries forward the research and development of a new jet engine and provides production capacity to produce the engine to meet the anticipated market. Now suppose an unusually large order is placed for the new engine. You must decide whether to increase production to meet the new order or to buy a number of parts from subcontractors. Here are a few advantages and disadvantages to each method.

Build in-house
   Advantages
      1. Close supervision of production standards and quality control.
      2. Increased production capacity if this order indicates an increase in the general level of business.
      3. All of the production profits are retained within the company.

---

[6] "U. S. Officials Believe SST Race Profitless," *Aviation Week*, **73**, No. 11, September 12, 1960, p. 40.
[7] "New Subsonic Jet Generation Forecast," *Aviation Week*, **81**, No. 10, September 5, 1964, p. 36.
[8] J. E. Gibson, "The Case against the Supersonic Transport," *Harpers*, **233**, No. 1394, July 1966, pp. 76 ff.

Disadvantages
1. Must pay fixed costs on increased production capacity even if it is idle after this one big order.
2. Labor contracts usually make layoffs of workers hired for this one job difficult. (This is also in accord with moral justice.)

Buy from outside vendor

Advantages
1. Develop second-source capacity to meet other peak-load demands. Government contracts often require this.
2. Small vendors are often ready to give quicker service than can be gotten from in-house production.
3. Small vendors sometimes have lower costs on short runs than in-house costs.

Disadvantages
1. Lack of quality control and lost profit opportunity must be watched.
2. Danger of building up a competitor for your prime markets.

Obviously the build-or-buy decision is a complex one and must be made on the basis of careful economic studies.

Present Economics

Many engineering decisions consist of a choice among various acceptable methods of doing a job. If it is assumed that the expenditures for any of the methods will be made in the same short period of time, the immediate or present cost of each is an accurate gauge of its comparative economy.

EXAMPLE 5.1

Suppose you are a production engineer faced with the problem of producing forty small, identical rigid couplings that will be used to join two odd-sized instrument shafts in a special order. There is no reason to suspect a repeat order in the near future so the job cost must stand by itself. The coupling is fairly simple and can be turned from round steel rod stock. Two machining methods present themselves. Table 5.1 shows the data for the metal lathe production and the automatic-screw machine production of the rigid coupling.

Table 5.1 Comparative Costs of Two Production Processes for a Particular Machined Item

	LATHE	AUTOMATIC SCREW MACHINE
Production rate	$4/hr	$18/hr
Machine charge	$5/hr	$25/hr
Set-up charge (labor)	——	$15
Operating charge (labor)	$5/hr	$3/hr
Material cost	Same	Same
Inspection cost	Same	Same
Tool cost	See text	See text

Since an automatic screw machine is a more complex and versatile device than a turret lathe, it is not surprising that its hourly cost is higher. A skilled machinist is needed to operate the lathe whereas a less skilled machine operator tends the automatic-screw machine. The set-up charge for the screw machine is to pay for the services of a highly skilled set-up man who initially adjusts its operation. The operator then keeps it supplied with raw material. Raw material and inspection costs would be independent of the method of production. The actual cutting tools for an automatic-screw machine would probably be more expensive than those for a lathe because the screw machine operates at a higher cutting speed. For this short run, however, tool wear will be negligible, and we can omit this cost. Now let us compute the cost of each method.

Lathe

$$\text{Machine cost:} \frac{40 \text{ pieces}}{4 \text{ pieces/hr}} \times \frac{\$5.00}{hr} = \$ \ 50.00$$

$$\text{Labor cost:} \quad 10 \text{ hr} \times \frac{\$5.00}{hr} \qquad = \$ \ 50.00$$

$$\text{Total} \qquad \overline{\$100.00}$$

Automatic-screw machine

$$\text{Machine cost:} \frac{40 \text{ pieces}}{18 \text{ pieces/hr}} \times \frac{\$25.00}{hr} = \$55.60$$

$$\text{Labor, set-up:} \qquad\qquad\qquad = \$15.00$$

$$\text{Labor, operator:} \ 2.25 \text{ hr} \times \frac{\$3.00}{hr} \quad = \$ \ 6.75$$

$$\text{Total} \qquad \overline{\$77.35}$$

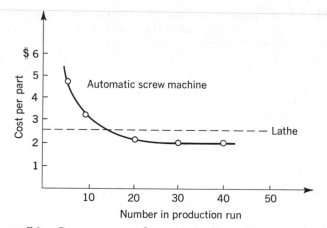

Figure 5.1. Comparative production costs for small rigid coupling.

The screw machine approach is obviously to be chosen. Figure 5.1 shows the cost per part for various length production runs. Set-up time on the lathe is essentially negligible, and for very long runs this fixed cost becomes less important for screw machine production. For this part the crossover point occurs for a production run of about sixteen. Below this number the lathe should be used, and for larger-size orders the screw machine is preferred.

Long-term Cost Studies

The cost of any operation occurring over any significant length of time must include the cost of borrowing money or interest as well as the cost of depreciation or wear of the equipment. Industrial engineers are often asked to make such economic studies. We will consider here one simple problem, which will bring out the concept of fixed costs and variable costs.

5.3   KELVIN'S LAW

Fixed costs are all those costs that are incurred by a plant or process independent of whether production goes on. These are the costs that pure scientists tend never to count. No doubt your professor can be encouraged to roundly damn the "overhead" costs the university so heartlessly subtracts from his research contracts. This is an example of a fixed cost. The cost of erecting a plant, maintaining it, providing for the aging of equipment, fire protection, insurance, and so on are all fixed costs.

To determine accurately the fixed costs of an operation is no simple matter, but we will approximate them in the following manner. Suppose the process under study does not yet exist. Suppose further that your company has no cash at its disposal. It will be your task to compute the total cost of erecting the entire process. Everything must be included. You then will go to a bank and present your proposal to an officer. If you have prepared it properly and the investment looks capable of sustaining itself, he will agree to a long-term loan, perhaps taking 20 years for repayment. Suppose to protect its investment, the bank requires you to take out an insurance and maintenance policy on the plant. It also arranges for your company to repay the loan in equal monthly installments. Each installment covers the payment on the principal plus the interest. After 20 years your company will have completely repaid the loan, and it will have an old and essentially worthless plant. Your total monthly payments, loan repayments, insurance, and maintenance are your fixed costs.

Variable costs or production costs are those costs directly assignable to the production of the product. These are the costs of raw material, labor, inspection, tool replacement, and so forth. These costs are usually obvious to an observer, and it is not likely that the concept of a production cost will be difficult to grasp. Actual evaluation of these costs, however, may require considerable study.

Quite often the engineer is asked to study the cost of an operation and to recommend the most economical operating point. At first thought it might be assumed that operation at maximum capacity of the machines would be most economical. Let us consider an actual case. F. Koenigsberger[9] discusses the cost of cutting metal, a basic machine shop operation important to all mechanical production. He studied the machining cost per work piece for various cutting speeds. In this problem certain charges are independent of the cutting speed or production rate. For example, the cost of preparing the work piece is independent of the rate at which production is set. Likewise, the cost of inspecting each

[9] F. Koenigsberger, "Cutting Metal More Efficiently," *New Scientist*, **21**, February 27, 1964, pp. 550–553.

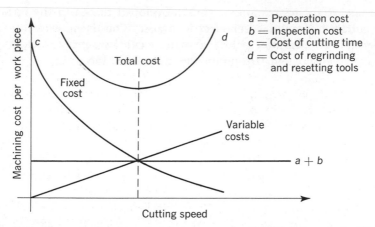

Figure 5.2.   The cost of cutting metal. An example of Kelvin's law. (*after Koenigsberger*)

piece to see if it meets standards is independent of cutting speed. These
costs are shown in Figure 5.2 as the horizontal line labeled $a + b$.

If a machine turns out twice as much finished work in a given time,
its productivity has doubled. Usually each machine in a plant is charged
with a certain constant cost per hour whether or not it is running. This
is in accord with our introduction to fixed costs. Thus it is conventional to
charge each piece of work with a cost depending on how long it is
on the machine. It seems logical then that the cost of cutting time should
go down as cutting speed goes up. This is shown as curve c in Figure
5.2.

If these three costs are all that are considered, it seems that the cutting
speed should be increased indefinitely to lower costs and increase profits.
A good engineer immediately suspects such a result. He knows that
almost invariably a trade-off is involved in which increased speed buys
certain advantages while at the same time incurring certain costs. The
cost of extra cutting speed in this example is the extra expense of regrind-
ing and resetting broken cutting tools. This curve is labeled d in Figure
5.2. The total cost of operating at any speed is found by adding the
values of the individual costs at that speed. Minimum total cost occurs
at the intersection of curves c and d. This fact is quite a general phenomenon and was noted by Lord Kelvin in 1881 and is now called *Kelvin's
law*.

The law proposed by Kelvin[10] was developed to obtain the optimum (that is, the minimum cost) electric transmission-line conductor cross-sectional area to carry a given current. It can be simply stated in the abstract. The value of x that minimizes $f(x)$ of the form

$$f(x) = k_1x + \frac{k_2}{x} \qquad (5.1)$$

is that value of x for which

$$k_1x = \frac{k_2}{x} \qquad (5.2)$$

Kelvin's law occurs and reoccurs through engineering. Sometimes the cost is not computed in terms of dollars. For example, in space-vehicle propulsion, weight is the item of most interest in cost studies. Mickelson[11] discusses the new concept of ion engines for space-vehicle propulsion. As the exhaust velocity of the ions is increased, greater propulsive effort is obtained. Thus, for a given mission the weight of required propellant is inversely proportional to exhaust velocity as shown in Figure 5.3. However, the weight of the electric power equipment to produce the high-velocity ions is a direct function of the desired velocity. Thus, the weight of the propulsion unit increases with exhaust velocity. The minimum total weight of the engine plus fuel is dictated by Kelvin's law.

EXAMPLE 5.2

Suppose that the average business traveler's time is worth $10 an hour. Suppose also that the total cost of operating an automobile varies as the square of its speed and that at 50 ml/hr it is 10 cents per mile. Assuming that traffic moves at the posted speed limit, for what maximum speed should a highway be designed that is to be used primarily by businessmen?

It is apparent that the faster our businessman travels the smaller will be his time cost to cover a given distance. However, the cost of operating

[10] W. Thomson, "On the Economy of Metal in Conductors of Electricity," *Report of British Association for the Advancement of Science,* 1881 (London: John Murray, 1882), pp. 526–528.

[11] A. Mickelson, "Electric Propulsion for Space Flight," *Aerospace Eng.,* **19**, No. 11, November 1960.

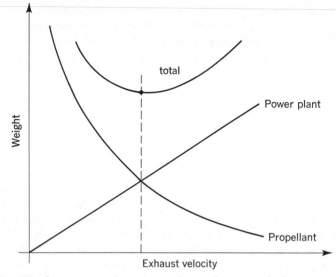

Figure 5.3.   Weight costs in electric propulsion of space vehicles. An example of Kelvin's law. (*after Mickelson*)

his car will increase as he increases his speed. This is a typical trade-off problem, and there should be some speed at which his total cost is at a minimum.

Let us first find an expression for the cost of the traveler's time. From the problem statement,

$$C_{\text{time}} = 10t \quad \text{(dollars)} \tag{5.3}$$

where the elapsed time, t, is measured in hours. This will not be as valuable as an expression in terms of velocity would be. On a trip of n mi at a velocity of v mi/hr, $t = n/v$. Thus, Equation 5.3 may be written as

$$C_{\text{time}} = \frac{10n}{v} \quad \text{(dollars)} \tag{5.4}$$

Now find an expression for the cost of operating the automobile. We are told that

$$C_{\text{auto}} = Knv^2 \tag{5.5}$$

where K is a constant of proportionality. We know the cost per mile C_{auto}/n at 50 mi/hr, and therefore we can find K.

$$\frac{C_{\text{auto}}}{n} = 0.1 \frac{\text{dollars}}{\text{mi}} = K(50)^2 \left(\frac{\text{mi}}{\text{hr}}\right)^2$$

Thus

$$K = 4 \times 10^{-5} \left(\frac{\text{dollars hr}^2}{\text{mi}^3} \right)$$

and Equation (5.5) becomes

$$C_{\text{auto}} = 4 \times 10^{-5} n v^2 \text{ (dollars)} \qquad (5.6)$$

The total cost is

$$C_{\text{total}} = C_{\text{time}} + C_{\text{auto}} = \frac{10n}{v} + 4 \times 10^{-5} n v^2 \qquad (5.7)$$

Here the fixed cost is inversely proportional to the velocity, but the variable cost is proportional to the square of the velocity rather than to the velocity itself. This is not precisely the situation proposed by Kelvin, so it will be interesting to see if the minimum of the total cost occurs where fixed costs equal variable costs.

There are two ways of finding the minimum of total costs. Differential calculus is a simple approach for those familiar with its mysteries. To find the minimum let

$$\frac{dC_{\text{total}}}{dv} = 0$$

Then[12]

$$\frac{dC_{\text{total}}}{dv} = \frac{-10n}{v^2} + 8 \times 10^{-5} n v = 0$$

and

$$v^3 = 1.25 \times 10^5$$

and

$$v = 50 \text{ mi/hr}$$

The more familiar way for many of us is to plot the graph of C_{total} versus v and determine the answer by inspection. Figure 5.4 shows such a plot. Indeed the minimum total cost is at a velocity of 50 ml/hr, but unfortunately this does not occur at the intersection of the fixed-cost and variable-cost curves. Thus, we must restrict Kelvin's law to the situation for which it was proposed, that is, when fixed cost is *inversely* proportional and variable cost *directly* proportional to the parameter that is under design.

[12] The economist calls the derivative of a cost the "marginal cost." Thus this equation may be interpreted as saying the sum of the marginal costs is zero.

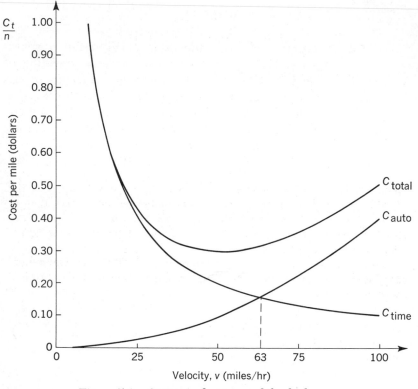

Figure 5.4. Optimum design speed for highway.

5.4 KELVIN'S LAW AND OPERATING EFFICIENCY

Kelvin's law and the concept of fixed costs is very important in the proper design of engineering projects. It is closely linked to the concept of operating efficiency, although this fact is seldom appreciated by those who are not engineers. We often hear that this or that process is very inefficient and that if engineers were only clever enough to double the absurdly low value of efficiency profits would be doubled. It usually surprises such critics to find that engineers stand ready not only to double the overall efficiency but to raise it by a factor of 4 or 5 and in some cases by even a factor of ten. Increasing operating efficiency— that is, reducing the operating cost—many increase fixed costs dispro- portionately and result in higher *total* costs. We will illustrate this point in the annealing furnace example in Chapter 6.

PROBLEMS

5.1 A kindly old professor hires student labor to install a split-rail fence on his property. He pays $5.00 for each section consisting of a post and two 10-ft rails. He buys 30 sections and 10 cans of wood preservative at $2.10 per can. He pays $1.50/hr for a hard-working student. On the first Saturday the hard-working student installs 10 sections of the fence in 8 hr. The kindly old professor is faced with the problem of hiring two students to finish the job on the following Saturday or to hire a gasoline-driven post-hole digger at $18.00 per 8-hr day. He estimates that one hard-working student could complete the job in 5 hr with the gasoline post-hole digger. Which option should he choose? What length fence represents the trade-off point between hand labor and automation?

5.2 I have purchased several acres of land in the vicinity of 48th Street and Fifth Avenue in New York City. My intention is to construct an office building at the lowest possible cost per floor. As the building gets higher, the cost of material decreases because of bulk rates, but the cost per floor increases because of increased labor and insurance. The following expressions may be taken as valid measures of these various costs.

$$C_1 = \frac{100,000}{f/2}$$

$$C_2 = 1000f$$

where C_1 = cost of materials (dollars)
C_2 = cost of labor and insurance (dollars)
f = number of floors

Assuming that the total cost is the sum of materials, labor, and insurance, find how high the building should be built.

5.3 Replot Figure 5.4 and superimpose the marginal costs, omitting the minus sign. The derivative or slope of the cost at any point may be found graphically or from the expression in Example 5.2. Are the marginal costs equal in magnitude at the optimum operating point? Under what conditions is this true? Is this a more general rule than Kelvin's law?

CHAPTER SIX

Energy in
Engineering Design

6.1 INTRODUCTION

Much of engineering has to do with obtaining and manipulating the mathematical descriptions of physical systems. Terms such as force, mass, position, and velocity help describe mechanical systems, and terms such as voltage and current are used to describe electrical systems. You will spend considerable time in later courses learning how to manipulate these and a number of other physical quantities such as entropy, enthalpy, temperature, stress, and strain. These and other "microconcepts" are all necessary for a detailed understanding of engineering devices. For a preliminary design or feasibility study, however, it is sometimes possible to postpone detailed consideration of such matters. Often the engineer can predict overall performance from careful use of such simple "macroconcepts" as energy, which is the subject of this chapter.

In fact, we can go further and say that an engineer should not undertake a detailed consideration of a particular device or element in a large-scale system until he has the results of a careful preliminary design. Often the engineer in charge accomplishes this task himself before handing out detailed design assignments. Other times the junior engineer finds himself a part of a specialized group that seems to operate independently of such considerations. Nevertheless, preliminary design is not only a part of engineering, it is perhaps the most critical step in the entire process. Hasty decisions made in the light of faulty information or lack of understanding of the real problem will return to haunt the engineer for the life of the project and may contribute to the reduction of profit and perhaps even the ultimate failure of the product.

6.2   ENERGY DEFINED

The word *work* when used by an engineer or physicist is a technical term. *Work* is defined as a force acting through a distance. If the force is exerted on a body and the body is moved by the force, then work is done on the body by the force.

The work done on a body is equal to the energy transferred to the body. This energy may be *dissipated* or used up in overcoming friction and ultimately turned to heat. On the other hand, it may be *conserved*. Energy may be conserved in either of two mechanical forms—kinetic energy or potential energy. *Potential energy* (PE) is that energy stored in a body solely by virtue of its relative position. *Kinetic energy* (KE) is that energy stored in a body by virtue of its relative velocity.

The concepts of *force* and *mass* are defined by Newton's second law of motion, but we will postpone discussing detailed application of Newton's law until a later course. For now, we merely note that we are discussing newtons of weight not kilograms of mass.

EXAMPLE 6.1

Calculate the PE stored in a weight of 10 newtons by lifting it 7 m above its initial resting place on top of a table. A force of 10 N is needed to counteract the weight due to gravity; thus,

$$\text{PE (added)} = 10 \text{ (N)} \times 7 \text{ (m)} = 70 \text{ (N} \cdot \text{m)} = 70 \text{ J}$$

Remember we can substitute the phrase "work done on the weight" for "potential energy stored in the weight." Note also that the calculation of PE implies a *datum plane* or *reference level*. With respect to the floor, we have several more joules of potential energy in the weight, and with respect to the bottom of a deep mine shaft we have several thousand joules of additional potential energy stored in it.

EXAMPLE 6.2

A rough block weighing 83 newtons is pushed 17 meters across a level floor. A force of 11 newtons is needed to keep the block in steady motion. What is the work done on the block?

Presumably the force is needed to overcome the friction between the block and the floor, and the energy expended or work done will appear as heat. It does not go into either PE or KE since the floor is level and the block is at rest when the force is removed. The weight of the block causes the friction, but we are told exactly what force is required to overcome it; thus,

$$\text{Work done on block} = 17 \text{ m} \times 11 \text{ N} = 187 \text{ J}$$

We cannot recover this energy because it is lost or dissipated in heat.

It can be shown that the KE, or that energy stored in a body by virtue of its velocity, is equal to

$$\text{KE} = \frac{wv^2}{2g} \tag{6.1}$$

where $w \triangleq$ weight of body (N)

$v \triangleq$ velocity of body with respect to a reference with which KE is calculated (m/s)

$g \triangleq$ acceleration of gravity; 9.8 (m/s²) is an average value at the surface of the earth

EXAMPLE 6.3

If the weight in Example 6.1 is released, with what KE does it strike the table top? There are at least two ways of doing this problem. We choose to emphasize the law of conservation of energy rather than computing velocity.

As the block falls, air friction slows it down slightly and heats the block. We will ignore this effect, although in some problems such as the re-entry of space vehicles, aerodynamic heating is a serious problem. If energy is conserved, the block loses 70 J of PE in falling to the table top, and all this is transformed into KE. Thus the answer is 70 J.[1]

Rotating bodies also store energy by virtue of their motion. The relation is

$$\text{KE} = \frac{J\omega^2}{2g} \tag{6.2}$$

where $J \triangleq$ moment of inertia $(\text{N} \cdot \text{m}^2)$
$\omega \triangleq$ angular velocity (rad/s).

EXAMPLE 6.4

A round steel shaft, 10 cm in diameter and 3 m long, is rolling across a smooth, level floor at 10 m/s. How high up an inclined ramp will it roll? This is a more complicated problem than it may appear to be. We could have confused it even more by stating the angle of the inclined ramp, but you will see that we do not need this value. Let us calculate the KE of the shaft as it is rolling and then convert this to PE.

An engineer's handbook gives the weight of steel as 7850 N/m³. Our shaft contains

$$\text{Volume} = \pi r^2 L = \pi (0.05 \text{ m})^2 \, 3 \text{ m} = 0.0236 \text{ m}^3$$

Now

$$7850 \text{ N/m}^3 \times 0.0236 \text{ m}^3 = 185 \text{ N}$$

Thus the kinetic energy due to translation is

$$\text{KE (translation)} = \frac{wv^2}{2g} = \frac{185 \text{ (N)} \times 100 \text{ (m/s)}^2}{2 \times 9.8 \text{ (m/s}^2)} = 944 \text{ J}$$

But the shaft is not sliding, it is turning. Thus it also has KE stored in its rotational velocity. The handbook tells us that the moment of inertia

---

[1] The alternate approach employs the equation of free-fall starting with zero initial velocity.

$$v = \sqrt{2gs} = \left(2 \times 9.8 \frac{\text{m}}{\text{s}^2} \times 7\text{m}\right)^{\frac{1}{2}} = 11.7 \frac{\text{m}}{\text{s}}$$

Now Equation (6.1) becomes

$$\text{KE} = \frac{wv^2}{2g} = \frac{10 \text{ (N)} \times (11.7)^2 \text{ (m}^2/\text{s}^2)}{2 \times 9.8 (\text{m/s}^2)} = 70 \text{ J}$$

for a round shaft is

$$J = \frac{wr^2}{2} = \frac{185 \ (N) \ (0.05 \ m)^2}{2} = 0.231 \ (N \cdot m^2)$$

$$\text{Angular velocity} = \frac{10 \ (m/s)}{.1\pi(m/\text{revolution})} \times \frac{2\pi(\text{radians})}{1(\text{rev})} = 200 \ (\text{rad/sec})$$

Thus from Equation (6.2),

$$\text{KE (rotation)} = \frac{J\omega^2}{2g} = \frac{0.231 \ (N \cdot m^2) \ 4 \times 10^4 \ (\text{rad/s})^2}{2 \times 9.8 \ m/s^2} = 471 \ J$$

$$\text{KE (total)} = \text{KE (translation)} + \text{KE (rotation)} = 1415 \ J$$

Since PE is height times weight, if all this KE is transformed to PE

$$\text{Height} = \frac{1415}{185} \frac{N \ m}{N} = 7.65 \ m \text{ above level surface}$$

6.3 FORMS OF ENERGY

We have introduced the law of conservation of energy and the concepts of kinetic energy and potential energy from the point of view of mechanics. There are many other forms of energy such as chemical, electrical, and nuclear. Table 6.1 lists a number of common forms.

All the various forms of energy are interchangeable, and the units could be the same for all. As a matter of practice, however, certain terms are more in vogue in one field than in others. Thus, we must be able to convert from one set of units to another. The following lists common energy equivalents.

1 joule = 1 watt-second
1 foot-pound = 1.356 joules
1 calorie (kilocalorie) = 4200 joules
1 British thermal unit = 0.252 calories
1 calorie = 3100 ft-lb
1 kilowatthour = 3412 British thermal units

EXAMPLE 6.5   IDEAL INSULATION THICKNESS FOR AN ANNEALING FURNACE

A good engineer trains himself to look for a trade-off curve in any design problem. If he obtains a result which seems to indicate that a

Table 6.1   Classification of Energy Forms

(from *Physics for the Inquiring Mind; the Methods, Nature, and Philosophy of Physical Science*, E. M. Rogers (1960): the table, "Classification of Energy Forms," p. 390. Reprinted by permission of Princeton University Press.)

NAME OF ENERGY	SHORT NAME	WHERE USED
Gravitational potential energy (often called potential energy)	Grav. P.E. (PE)	Whenever a load is raised, there is a gain of gravitational PE stored in the field.
Strain energy (often called simply potential energy)	Strain E. (PE)	When a spring, or any other elastic material, is bent, stretched, twisted, or compressed, it stores up strain energy.
Kinetic energy	KE	The energy of motion of body. We can show that KE $= (\frac{1}{2})$ MASS SPEED^2.
Rotational kinetic energy or spin energy	Spin E.	Each part of a spinning object is moving and therefore has some KE. Spin Energy is the total of these KE's.
Heat energy	Heat	We can show that heat can be exchanged with KE, PE, and so forth. We now regard heat as the energy of molecular motions.
Chemical energy or molecular energy (should be called atomic energy)	Chemical E.	Fireworks, explosives, fuels, and food can release heat and other forms of energy in chemical changes. We picture them holding "chemical energy" stored "between atoms."
Molecular energy of melting and evaporation	Latent heat	Extra heat is taken in, in melting or in evaporation. It does not make temperature rise but is stored in molecular fields.
Electric energy Magnetic energy	Electric E. Magnetic E.	Electric circuits, charged capacitors, electromagnets involve electric energy and magnetic energy.

Table 6.1 Classification of Energy Forms (Continued)

NAME OF ENERGY	SHORT NAME	WHERE USED
Electromagnetic energy	E-ME.	The energy may reside in the electric and magnetic fields, which are closely connected.
Electromagnetic-wave energy	E-M wave E.	Electromagnetic waves involve traveling electric and magnetic fields. They include visible light, infrared, ultraviolet, x-rays, and radio waves of all wavelengths.
Radiation energy (including light energy)	Radiation (light E.)	Radiation includes light and all other electromagnetic waves.
Wave energy (including light and sound and ocean waves)	Wave E. (sound E.) (PE + KE)	Most waves carry energy (for example, light, sound, and ocean waves).
Nuclear energy	Nuclear E.	Released in nuclear changes: radioactivity, nuclear fission, and nuclear fusion.

certain critical dimension should grow without bound or shrink to zero, he becomes suspicious of the result. In this example we will compute the ideal insulation thickness for a furnace used to anneal brass. It is apparent that as the insulation thickness is increased, the heat loss through the walls is decreased. The trade-off concept is operative here because the insulation itself costs money to install.

The inside dimensions of the furnace are 70 ft by 40 ft by 6 ft. The insulation is Sil-O-Cel brick. There are two 8-ft by 6-ft openings through which the conveyor runs. The conveyor moves at 4.5 ft/min. The conveyor weighs 12 lb/ft and is made of steel. The conveyor temperature is 180°F at the outlet. The conveyor carries 10,000 lb of brass through the furnace per hour. Air at 70°F moves into the furnace through the inlet and outlet openings. Assume three complete changes of air per hour. The following list gives the data needed for the computation.

1. Specific heats
   Brass = 0.092 (Btu)/(lb) (°F)
   Steel = 0.125 (Btu)9/(lb) (°F)
   Air = 0.245 (Btu/(lb) (°F)

2.   At 70°F and atmospheric pressure the weight of air is 0.075 lb/ft³.

3.   Door loss due to radiation is 0.4 Kwhr/ft² of opening area per hour.

4.   Sil-O-Cel brick size is 3 in. by 4 in. by 8 in. Each brick costs 5 cents, and costs 10 cents to install. Its thermal conductivity is 0.58 (Btu) in./ft² (°F) (hr).

5.   Electrical energy costs $0.02/Kwhr on a bulk basis.

6.   Bank financing can be obtained for a total amortization of 15 percent/yr.

The cost of operating the furnace for one hour can be computed by adding together all of the heat losses.

1.   *Energy required to heat brass per hour.*

It is necessary only to multiply the number of pounds of brass handled by the temperature differential and by the specific heat to obtain the energy absorbed in a material.

$$10,000 \frac{lb}{hr} \times 680°F \times 0.092 \frac{Btu}{lb\ °F} = 6.2 \times 10^5 \frac{Btu}{hr}$$

or

$$6.2 \times 10^5 \frac{Btu}{hr} \times \frac{1\ Kwhr}{3412\ Btu} = 183.2 \frac{Kwhr}{hr}$$

2.   *Energy required to heat conveyor per hour.*

$$12 \frac{lb}{ft} \times 4.5 \frac{ft}{min} \times 60 \frac{min}{hr} \times 0.125 \frac{Btu}{lb\ °F} \times 570°F \times \frac{1\ Kwhr}{3412\ Btu}$$
$$= 67.6 \frac{Kwhr}{hr}$$

3.   *Energy required to heat air per hour.*

$$70\ ft \times 40\ ft \times 6\ ft \times 3 \frac{changes}{hr} \times 680°F \times 0.075 \frac{lb}{ft^3} \times 0.245 \frac{Btu}{lb\ °F}$$
$$\times \frac{1\ Kwhr}{3412\ Btu} = 184.5 \frac{Kwhr}{hr}$$

4.   *Door loss per hour.*

$$6\ ft \times 8\ ft \times 2 \times 0.4 \frac{Kwhr}{ft^2\ hr} = 38.4 \frac{Kwhr}{hr}$$

5.   *Conduction loss through Sil-O-Cel brick* is given in terms of feet squared of surface exposed to the heat, the inches of thickness, and the

temperature differential. The area of the furnace is approximately (top, bottom, two ends, and two sides) 6920 ft². The heat loss is

$$6920 \text{ ft}^2 \times 680°\text{F} \times 0.58 \frac{(\text{Btu}) (\text{in.})}{\text{ft}^2 \,°\text{F hr}} \times \frac{1 \text{ Kwhr}}{3412 \text{ Btu}} \times \frac{1}{I \text{ in.}} = \frac{800 \text{ Kwhr}}{I \text{ hr}}$$

where I is the thickness of the insulation in inches. This number remains to be determined.

6. For three hundred 8-hour working days per year the energy charge for the first four items will be

$$(183.2 + 67.6 + 184.5 + 38.4) \frac{\text{Kwhr}}{\text{hr}} - 300 \frac{\text{days}}{\text{yr}} \times \frac{8 \text{ hr}}{\text{day}} \times \frac{\$0.02}{\text{Kwhr}}$$

$$= 22737.60 \frac{\text{dollars}}{\text{yr}}$$

7. *For conduction losses.*

$$\frac{800}{I} \frac{\text{Kwhr}}{\text{hr}} \times \frac{300 \text{ days}}{\text{yr}} \times \frac{8 \text{ hr}}{\text{day}} \times \frac{\$0.02}{\text{Kwhr}} = \frac{38400}{I} \frac{\text{dollars}}{\text{yr}}$$

Item (6) will be independent of the thickness of insulation so it need not be considered in the calculation for the optimum thickness of the insulating bricks.

8. *Cost of bricks.*

To simplify the calculations, find the volume of bricks by multiplying the surface area (6920 ft²) by thickness. This ignores the corner effect. We can compute the cost of brick for a given volume from the data given. The brick costs

$$\frac{\$0.15}{3 \text{ in.} \times 4 \text{ in.} \times 8 \text{ in.}} = \frac{\$0.00156}{\text{in.}^3}$$

Thus, the total cost of installing the insulation is

$$6920 \text{ ft}^2 \times \frac{144 \text{ in.}^2}{\text{ft}^2} \times I \text{ in.} \times \frac{\$0.00156}{\text{in.}^3} = 1557 \, I \text{ (dollars)}$$

Amortize this at 15 percent/yr. Then

$$1557 \, I \text{ dollars} \times \frac{\$0.15}{\text{yr}} = 233.5 \, I \frac{\text{dollars}}{\text{yr}}$$

9. Now plot items (7) and (8) to find the minimum cost thickness as shown in Figure 6.1. Apparently the optimum thickness is about 13 in. The operating costs due to conduction losses are then about $3000/yr. Adding the other operating costs from item (6) yields

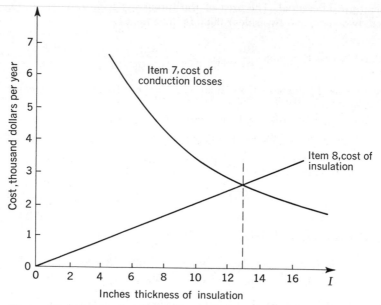

Figure 6.1. Kelvin's law for insulation thickness of annealing furnace.

$25,737.60/yr operating cost. The cost of the bricks is only one part of the total fixed cost of the furnace. Thus, we would need additional information to compute the total fixed cost of the furnace.

6.4 POWER

Power is the rate at which work is done or energy is transferred. Quite often such rates are more convenient to work with than the total energy itself. Given below is a short list of power conversion factors.

> 1 watt = 1 J/s
> 1 horsepower = 550 ft lb/s = 33,000 ft lb/min
> 1 horsepower = 746 W
> 1 watt = 0.737 ft lb/s

The unit of power called *horsepower* was developed for mechanical applications. The mechanical engineer often finds use for a relation among torque or twisting force, speed, and energy.

$$\text{Horsepower} = \frac{2\pi N T}{33{,}000}$$

where $N \triangleq$ revolutions per minute (r/min)
$T \triangleq$ torque (ft lb)

The electrical engineer is accustomed to use the watt or kilowatt ($1\,\text{kW} = 1000\,\text{W}$) as a unit of power.

$$\text{Watts} = EI = I^2 R = \frac{E^2}{R}$$

where $E \triangleq$ voltage across an element (V)
$I \triangleq$ current through an element (A)
$R \triangleq$ resistance of an element (Ω)

EXAMPLE 6.6

Suppose the block in Example 6.2 moves the 17 m in 3.5 s. At what rate is the energy dissipated?

$$\text{Power} = \frac{\text{energy}}{\text{time}} = \frac{187\,\text{J}}{3.5\,\text{s}} = 53.4\,\frac{\text{J}}{\text{s}} = 53.4\,\text{W}$$

This is a perfectly good answer, but we will also convert to horsepower and foot-pounds per second using the list of power conversion factors.

$$53.4\,\text{W} \times \frac{1\,\text{hp}}{746\,\text{W}} = 0.0716\,\text{hp}$$

$$53.4\,\text{W} \times 0.737\,\frac{\text{ft lb/s}}{\text{W}} = 39.4\,\text{ft lb/s}$$

6.5 EFFICIENCY AND ENERGY BALANCE

One of the primary concerns of the engineer, especially in preliminary design, is the overall efficiency of the proposed unit. This will determine the profit or loss and is one of a small number of basic questions on which the ultimate decision to go forward will depend. The engineer often determines the efficiency by running simple energy-balance calculations on the elements of the overall system.

We have said that energy is conserved and that it may be converted from one form to another. In theory this is true (a meaningless, academic statement that will wear on your ears after awhile), but in practice each time energy is converted from one form to another some portion of the total is changed to heat energy. We find it difficult or impossible to prevent some of this heat energy from leaking into the environment. For example, when we dropped the block onto the table, air friction heated the air and the block. That heat energy was lost. How could you prevent that loss? "Well," you say, "I would drop it in a vacuum." But then the motor on the vacuum pump heats up. In general we may conclude that all of the energy put into a system does not end up in a useful form. The proportion that does is called the efficiency of the unit.

EXAMPLE 6.7   EFFICIENCY OF AUTOMOBILE ENGINE

My 1964 Corvair weighs 2792 lb loaded, and on a turnpike trip averaging 50 mi/hr I measured 25.1 mi/gal. To find the force required to propel the car at 50 mi/hr we perform a deceleration test. At a constant speed, say 60 mi/hr, throw the car into neutral, and note the time required to decelerate to 40 mi/hr. These values were chosen to center around 50 mi/hr and to provide a sufficient range in order to make timing easy. The average of several runs showed

$$\frac{60 \text{ mi/hr} - 40 \text{ mi/hr}}{20 \text{ s}} = 1 \text{ mi/hr per s} \tag{6.3}$$

This is a mixed unit and not much good for anything. Thus, convert it to

$$1 \frac{\text{mi}}{\text{hr, s}} \times \frac{5280 \text{ ft}}{1 \text{ mi}} \times \frac{1 \text{ hr}}{3600 \text{ s}} = 1.47 \frac{\text{ft}}{\text{s}^2} \tag{6.4}$$

By consulting a chemical engineering handbook we find that gasoline contains 30,000 cal/gal. Find the efficiency of the engine if the useful output is defined as providing the force required for constant velocity of the automobile.

First, we will compute the force required to maintain a constant speed by Newton's law. Newton proposed a relation among force, weight, and change in velocity (acceleration or deceleration). We have the weight of the car and the change in velocity; therefore we can compute the force needed to cause this change. Newton's law yields

$$f = \frac{w}{g}\, a = \frac{2792\ \text{(lb)}}{32.2\ \text{(ft/s}^2)} \times 1.47\ \frac{\text{ft}}{\text{s}^2} = 127.6\ \text{lb} \qquad (6.5)$$

Presumably the engine must provide a force equal to the deceleration force in order to maintain a constant speed. To drive 1 mile against this deceleration force requires

$$127.6\ \text{lb} \times 5280\ \frac{\text{ft}}{\text{mi}} = 6.74 \times 10^5\ \frac{\text{ft lb}}{\text{mi}}$$

Since this force is exerted through the distance, this figure is the work done per mile or the useful energy per mile. Now compute the chemical energy released per mile by the gasoline to find the total energy

$$\frac{1}{25.1}\ \frac{\text{gal}}{\text{mi}} \times 30{,}000\ \frac{\text{cal}}{\text{gal}} = 1195\ \frac{\text{cal}}{\text{mi}} \qquad (6.6)$$

Now convert the calories to foot-pounds

$$1195\ \frac{\text{cal}}{\text{mi}} \times 3100\ \frac{\text{ft lb}}{\text{cal}} = 3.7 \times 10^6\ \frac{\text{ft lb}}{\text{mi}} \qquad (6.7)$$

Thus the efficiency of the engine and power train is

$$\text{Percent efficiency} = \frac{\text{output}}{\text{input}} \times 100 = \frac{6.74 \times 10^5}{3.7 \times 10^6} \times 100$$

$$= 18.2\ \text{percent} \qquad (6.8)$$

6.6 ENERGY FLOW DIAGRAMS

A convenient way of illustrating the energy balance in a device is the energy flow diagram. Suppose we take as an example, the self-excited dc generator discussed in Chapter 3 and construct such a diagram. If you skipped Example 3.3 because it looked complicated you should go back now and check it out.

EXAMPLE 6.8 ENERGY FLOW DIAGRAM FOR MOTOR-GENERATOR SET

Figure 6.2 shows a sketch of a common form of motor-generator set for emergency electric-power use. If the generator is in the low- or

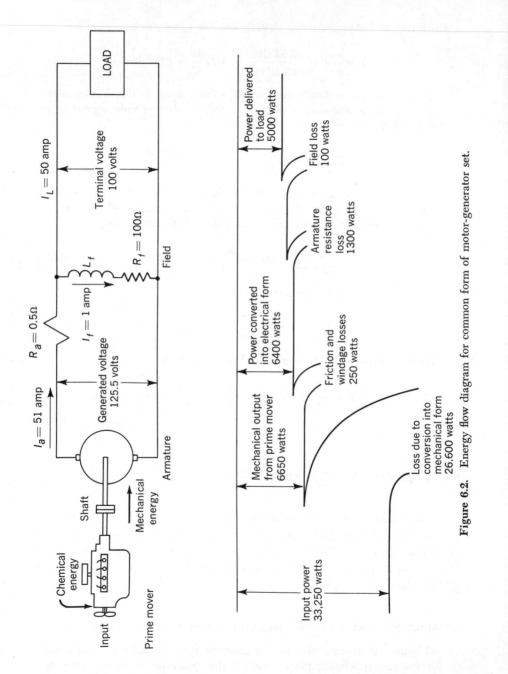

Figure 6.2. Energy flow diagram for common form of motor-generator set.

medium-power range—say, from 5 to 50 kW—a gasoline motor may be used, but for large systems a diesel motor or jet engine is often employed.

Suppose we are told that the unit consumes 0.954 gal of gasoline for each hour of full-load operation, and that the conversion efficiency of the "prime mover" is 20 percent. The phrase "prime mover" is a misnomer. It is really an energy-conversion device for converting energy in chemical form into mechanical (kinetic) energy. Converting into electrical units yields

$$0.954\,\frac{\text{gal}}{\text{hr}} \times \frac{30,000\ \text{cal}}{\text{gal}} \times \frac{1\ \text{Btu}}{0.252\ \text{cal}} \times \frac{1\ \text{kWh}}{3412\ \text{Btu}} = 33.25\ \text{kW}$$

This is placed on the input position of the energy flow (power) chart. The efficiency of conversion to mechanical form is given as 20 percent. Thus $(0.8)(33250) = 26,000$ W are lost in the prime mover in the form of heat, and 6650 W are delivered to the shaft. Tests indicate that 250 W are used in overcoming friction in bearings and windage effects in the generator. The difference, 6400 W, is converted into electrical form in the armature of the generator. The power converted to electrical form is also equal to the product of the armature current and generated voltage. Internal to the armature there is a loss due to the armature current flowing in the armature resistance R_a.

$$\text{Armature resistance loss} = I_a{}^2 R_a = (51)^2 0.5 = 1300\ \text{W}$$

There is an additional loss in the field due to the current required to establish the magnetic field.

$$\text{Field loss} = I_f{}^2 R_f = (1)^2 100 = E_t I_f = (100)(1) = 100\ \text{W}$$

The remainder of 5000 W is delivered to the load. The power diagram helps to simplify energy balance and efficiency calculations as well as to illustrate the operation of the device. The efficiency from input shaft of the generator to load terminals is

$$\text{Electrical efficiency} = \frac{5000\ \text{W}}{6650\ \text{W}} \times 100 = 75.3\ \text{percent}$$

and

$$\text{Overall efficiency} = \frac{5000\ \text{W}}{33,250\ \text{W}} \times 100 = 15\ \text{percent}$$

PROBLEMS

6.1 By exerting a constant force of 12.0 lb on a rope attached to a sled, a man pulls the sled across ice on the surface of a pond. If the rope makes an angle of 45° with the direction of motion, how much work does the man do in moving the sled a distance of 90.0 ft?

6.2   An elevator cage has a weight of (1000/9.82)N. If frictional effects are negligible, how much work is done in raising the cage 50 m at a constant speed?

6.3   An automobile weighing 3220 lb has an instantaneous velocity of 60 ft/s southward. What is the kinetic energy of the automobile? If frictional losses were negligible, how much work was done in giving the automobile this velocity?

6.4   A dc lifting motor has a full-load efficiency of 70 percent. If the motor is fully loaded, a line current of 50 A flows into it while a voltage of 200 V is applied. The full load consists of a 2000-lb weight to be lifted. How high can the motor lift the weight in 10 s?

6.5   Construct an energy flow chart for the annealing furnace in Example 6.5. Is "efficiency" a meaningful concept here?

6.6   A motor-generator set is used to change 110 volt, 60 Hertz electrical power into 27 volt, 400 Hertz power. Of the input power of 5.0 kilowatts, 20 percent is lost in the resistance of the motor's armature windings and 3 percent is lost in the resistance of the motor's field windings. The rest goes into mechanical power input to the generator. Of the mechanical power running the generator, 1 percent is lost in friction to the bearings, 21 percent is lost in the resistance of the generator's armature windings, and 4 percent is lost in the resistance of the generators' field windings. How much power does the set produce at 400 Hertz? What is the overall efficiency of the system?

CHAPTER SEVEN

Thermodynamics in Engineering Design

7.1 INTRODUCTION

Thermodynamics can be defined as the science that deals with heat and work and those properties of substances that bear a relation to heat and work. Like all sciences, the basis of thermodynamics is experimental observation. In thermodynamics these findings have been formalized into three laws, which are known as the first, second, and third laws of thermodynamics.[1]

[1] G. J. Van Wylen, *Thermodynamics* (New York: John Wiley and Sons, Inc., 1959), p. 13.

The engineer has a basic concern for energy and since energy so often appears in the form of heat, he in turn must have a basic concern for heat and its effect. This concern is dignified by the term thermodynamics. During the Middle Ages, heat was thought of as a mysterious substance. We read of "caloric flow" in the old manuscripts. Count Rumford, a brilliant engineer but apparently a man completely without conscience, first noted the mechanical equivalence of heat while he watched cannon bores being drilled in a little Prussian duchy to which he had sold himself as commander-in-chief of the armed forces. Gradually a more rational understanding of heat grew up, until in the present day, it is one of the more precisely understood scientific tools of the engineer.

7.2   THERMODYNAMIC SYSTEMS

A *thermodynamic system* is an arbitrary collection of matter and space, defined for the convenience of analysis. A *closed system* is one in which mass cannot cross the system boundary, and an *open system* is one in which mass can cross the boundary. The engineer draws the system boundary to suit his convenience. It is even proper to allow the system to have a moving boundary as, for example, the piston head in a cylinder. The engineer can compute the rates at which mass, heat, and work move across the boundary of the system and compute the efficiencies involved in such transfers. This overall view—combined with the power of the general principles of thermodynamics, called "laws"—makes an appealing tool for preliminary design.

A sign convention has been adopted for analysis of thermodynamic systems. Heat, mass, and work that move across the boundary *into* the system are defined as *positive*. (See Figure 7.1.) The total internal energy U of a system is the energy contained within its boundaries. It is obtained in three ways.

1. *Heat*, noted as Q, is that energy transferred across the boundary as a result of a temperature difference.
2. *Work*, noted at W, is a force acting through a distance.
3. *Mass transfer*, noted as E_m, is the energy transferred across the boundary in the form of mass.

The specific interrelationship of these quantities will be discussed later when we get to the laws of thermodynamics.

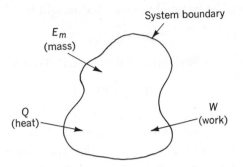

Figure 7.1.   The sign convention in thermodynamic systems.

One of the important details of thermodynamic systems is that they can have moving boundaries. Suppose we have a cylinder as shown in Figure 7.2 with a perfectly fitting movable piston. The system consists of the cylinder with the heavy piston, which presses down on the gas inside. We will assume that the system is in equilibrium. That is, the position of the piston is such that its weight is equal to the pressure of the compressed gas. Now let us calculate the work done on the system by adding a small additional weight that moves the piston down a small distance ΔL and does not change the temperature. Work is force times distance. The force exerted by the gas on the piston is

$$F = pA \tag{7.1}$$

where $p \triangleq$ pressure of gas (lb/in.^{2})

   $A \triangleq$ area of piston (in.^{2})

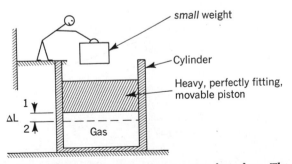

Figure 7.2.   A thermodynamic system with a moving boundary. The piston moves without friction.

The work done on the system by the added weight is

$$W = pA\,\Delta L \qquad (7.2)$$

But $A\Delta L$ is the change in volume of the gas ΔV. Thus

$$W = p\Delta V \qquad (7.3)$$

Of course, neither p nor V are constant. As the volume is reduced the pressure is increased. We have operated between points 1 and 2 on the curve shown in Figure 7.3. Note that the pressure is not constant between these two points. We insisted that only a *small* weight be added so that the volume would change only slightly ΔV, and therefore an average value of p could be used in Equation (7.3) without any great error.

Note from Equation (7.3) that the area under the curve between points 1 and 2 can be interpreted as the work done on the system. There is no approximation if the shape of the curve is correctly accounted for; points 1 and 2 can then be wide apart. To emphasize this point, consider the process illustrated in Figure 7.4. Suppose the process starts at point 1. The gas is compressed and the process proceeds along path (a) to point 2. The total area under curve (a) between 1 and 2 is positive work, since it represents energy transferred across the boundary *into* the system. Now the gas is allowed to expand, and suppose the process proceeds along path (b) to point 1. The area under path (b) is negative work done by the system. The area between the two curves represents

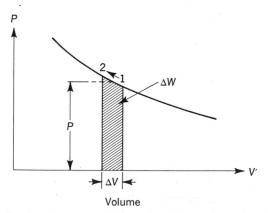

Figure 7.3. Graphical interpretation of work done on gas by compressing it. A P-V diagram.

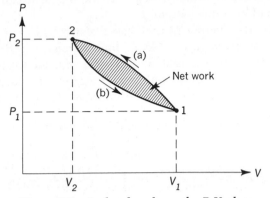

Figure 7.4.   A closed cycle on the P-V plane.

the net work. In this case it is positive, which means the system absorbs energy through the mechanism of work by being put through this cycle. Let us add a caution at this point. The area under a p-v curve is *not* always equal to work. In fact it is true only in a quasistatic process which involves a moving boundary of a closed system.

Let us define the terms process and cycle. A *process* is any event or series of events in which energy is transferred across the boundary of a thermodynamic system. Usually we define specific kinds of processes such as adiabatic, isothermal, or isentropic in which one or another of the important thermodynamic quantities is held constant. A *cycle* is a series of processes that are executed by the system and following which the final state of the system is equal to the initial state. The *state* of a system may be defined as the condition of its internal energy, *U.*

7.3 HEAT

After considerable drilling through high school and college you have probably accepted the fact that the term "work" has a technical meaning quite different from the meaning given it in everyday affairs. I regret to say that we must now start the same process with the word *heat.*

Heat and work have a number of functional similarities. They are both transient phenomena that indicate a transfer of energy. A body (system) does not store work or heat.[2] Work and heat can be observed only at the boundary of the system.

Heat is given the symbol Q and has the units Btu's in the English system and watt-seconds in the MKSA unit system. The British thermal unit is the amount of heat that must be transferred to one pound of water to raise it one degree fahrenheit under standard conditions. Table 7.1 gives several common conversions involving heat transfer.

Table 7.1   Heat Unit Conversions

$$1 \text{ Btu} = \overset{778}{\cancel{788}} \text{ ft lb}$$

$$1 \text{ horsepower} = 33{,}000 \text{ ft lb/min} = 42.4 \text{ Btu/min} = 2545 \text{ Btu/hr}$$

$$1 \text{ kilowatt} = 44{,}200 \text{ ft lb/min} = 56.9 \text{ Btu/min} = 3412 \text{ Btu/hr}$$

Since heat and work are both manifestations of energy transfer, it seems reasonable to find that we can convert readily from heat units to work units. A process in which there is no heat transfer $(Q = 0)$ is called *adiabatic*.

Temperature is not the same as heat. Two bodies at the same temperature may contain different energies. (Bodies do not *contain* heat, they transfer heat when brought in contact with surroundings at a different temperature.)

The Fahrenheit temperature scale is in common usage and is based on the boiling point of water. The Rankine scale uses Fahrenheit divisions but is an absolute scale in that its zero point is at absolute zero (that theoretical point at which all motion ceases). Centigrade is a relative scale designed to put 100 divisions between the freezing point and boiling point of water. The Kelvin scale is an absolute scale using Centigrade divisions. Table 7.2 compares these scales. All thermodynamic calculations are made with one of the two *absolute scales*.

Table 7.2   Temperature Scale Comparisons

	ABSOLUTE ZERO	FREEZING POINT OF WATER	BOILING POINT OF WATER
Fahrenheit	$-460°F$	$32°F$	$212°F$
Rankine	$0°R$	$492°R$	$672°R$
Centigrade	$-273°C$	$0°C$	$100°C$
Kelvin	$0°K$	$273°K$	$373°K$

[2] Technically we say that heat and work are path functions and not point functions. One needs to examine the path by which the system gets from point 1 to point 2 on the p-V diagram, for example, in order to calculate the work done.

7.4   THE THREE LAWS OF THERMODYNAMICS

The quotation which opens this chapter points out that the laws of thermodynamics are the result of observational experience. A *law* of science in this sense then must be simple, understandable, and acceptable to any rational person, and, it must be general in its application. Such laws, however, are never absolute and do not spring from authoritarianism. One cannot "prove" these laws and one cannot invoke them to contradict an argument which (knowingly) contravenes them.

The first law of thermodynamics is the law of conservation of energy. It implies that energy may be freely converted from one form to another while the net total energy remains constant. Since the thermodynamicist is so concerned with heat, work, and systems, he sometimes phrases the first law in such terms. For example, Spalding and Cole state it as follows: "When a system executes a cyclic process, the algebraic sum of the work transfers is proportional to the algebraic sum of the heat transfers."

For a thermodynamic system the first law may be expressed as

$$U_f - U_i = \Delta U = Q + W + E_m$$

That is, the change in internal energy of a system is the sum of heat, work, and mass transfers across its boundary. A closed system is defined as one in which $E_m = 0$. A *thermodynamic cycle* is defined as a series of thermodynamic processes which if executed consecutively will cause the final state of the working substance to be identical to its initial state. Therefore, in a thermodynamic cycle, the change in internal energy is zero.

EXAMPLE 7.1

Suppose a closed thermodynamic system is put through a cycle in which a net 100 W s of heat is added to the system. What other energy transfer mechanism must be involved? Because this is a closed system,

$$E_m = 0$$

Furthermore, in a cycle

$$\Delta U = 0$$

Thus, applying the first law,

$$W = -Q = -100 \text{ W s}$$

The minus sign indicates the system has done work on its environment.

EXAMPLE 7.2

Suppose the blowtorch in Problem 7.1 added 100 Btu of heat to the gas in that constant pressure (isobaric?) process. What is the state of the system at the end of the process? With a closed system the first law is

$$\Delta U = Q + W$$

Thus

$$\Delta U = 100 \text{ Btu} + p(V_i - V_f)$$
$$= 100 \text{ Btu} + 20 \left(\frac{\text{lb}}{\text{in.}^2}\right) \times (1 - 3)(\text{ft}^3)144 \left(\frac{\text{in.}^2}{\text{ft}^2}\right) \frac{1}{778} \left(\frac{\text{Btu}}{\text{ft lb}}\right)$$
$$= 100 \text{ Btu} - 7.4 \text{ Btu}$$
$$\Delta U = 92.6 \text{ Btu}$$

This indicates that the internal energy of the gas is greater at the end of the process than at the beginning.

The second law of thermodynamics is more restrictive in nature than the first; it deals specifically with heat transfer. The second law as formulated by Clausius states that it is impossible to construct a device that operates in a cycle and produces no effect other than the transfer of heat from a cooler body to a warmer one. The law rules out a 100-percent efficient heat engine. It also implies that it is impossible to build a heat pump that operates without an input of work. In effect, this law states that any form of perpetual-motion machine is impossible.

Two manifestations of the second law are: first, heat transfer takes place only in the direction of decreasing temperature, and, second, a work transfer is always accompanied by a heat transfer.

The third law of thermodynamics involves the concept of entropy. In Chapter 8, the word *entropy* is used to designate a measure of disorganization or lack of regularity of pattern. Entropy, denoted by the symbol S, in a thermodynamic sense means exactly this same thing. In fact, it is possible to relate the concepts of information theory to statistical thermodynamics using the concept of entropy. The third law as formulated by Planck states that the entropy (disorganization) of a pure substance is zero at a temperature of absolute zero.

We can define entropy analytically as the change in heat per unit temperature in a reversible process.[3]

$$\Delta S = \left(\frac{\Delta Q}{T}\right)_{\text{reversible process}}$$

A constant entropy process is called isentropic.

To the uninitiated reader these laws may appear either so obvious or so obscure that their importance is difficult to appreciate. We will consider the second law in more detail to better illustrate its importance for just this reason.

7.5 THE CARNOT CYCLE

The second law states that a 100-percent efficient heat engine is impossible. Sadi Carnot, a French engineer who formulated the second law in 1824, asked himself: Is it possible to state what the upper limit of efficiency is? The answer turns out to be yes.

The thermodynamic efficiency of a heat engine may be defined as

$$\eta_{\text{thermal}} = \frac{\text{useful energy output}}{\text{required energy input}} \tag{7.4}$$

For a cycle of a closed thermodynamic system the first law is

$$Q = Q_H - Q_L = -W \tag{7.5}$$

Thus Equation (7.4) becomes

$$\eta_{\text{thermal}} = \frac{-W}{Q_H} = \frac{Q_H - Q_L}{Q_H} = 1 - \frac{Q_L}{Q_H} \tag{7.6}$$

Now since the amount of heat transferred in an ideal, reversible process is directly proportional to the temperature drop,[4]

$$\frac{T_H}{T_L} = \frac{Q_H}{Q_L} \tag{7.7}$$

[3] It is a mark of naiveté to say, "But what *is* entropy?" Of course you do not understand entropy. The *real* problem is that you do not understand work, heat, temperature, energy, and so forth—*and you think you do.*

[4] Play this one under protest. In a reversible process all elements may be returned unchanged from the final state to the initial state.

Equation (7.7) may be substituted in Equation (7.6) to yield

$$\eta_{\text{thermal}} = 1 - \frac{T_L}{T_H} \tag{7.8}$$

The Carnot cycle is a description of an ideal theoretical heat engine that could not be built in reality. The purpose of the cycle is to illustrate the maximum obtainable efficiency of a device that does not break any thermodynamic laws. Van Wylen gives an example of a Carnot cycle in a steam-boiler turbine plant as shown in Figure 7.5. The Carnot cycle draws its energy from a high temperature source. The working substance of the engine is assumed to be a pure substance, such as steam. The cycle consists of four thermodynamic processes, which when executed consecutively will return the substance to its starting point. The first process is to change water into steam in the boiler by the addition of heat Q_H, from the high temperature source. This must be done in a very special way. The temperature must not change while the water changes to vapor. This will then be a reversible, isothermal process.[5]

The second process occurs in the turbine. It occurs without heat transfer and is thus adiabatic. Like all other processes in a Carnot cycle, it must be reversible. The steam drops in pressure and temperature as it expands and produces work in turning the turbine.

Now the temperature of the steam has dropped to the value of the low temperature reservoir. It enters the condenser and at constant temperature, heat, Q_L, is extracted (reversible, isothermal process), thus turning the steam back (almost completely) to water in its liquid phase.[5] Q_L is lost from the cycle in the condenser. It cannot be recovered because by the second law, heat cannot be made to flow from the low temperature reservoir to the high temperature reservoir without the use of work. In fact to directly compress the steam at the turbine outlet without removing Q_L in an isothermal manner would require precisely the same amount of work into the system as was removed from the turbine, resulting in a net output of zero.

Finally the water is compressed completely to liquid and is raised in pressure in the pump in a reversible, adiabatic manner (without allowing heat to escape) to its original pressure. This raises the temperature of the water back up to the temperature of the high temperature

[5] Because during this process the working substance is a mixture of liquid and vapor states, the pressure remains constant. This is not always so in a Carnot cycle.

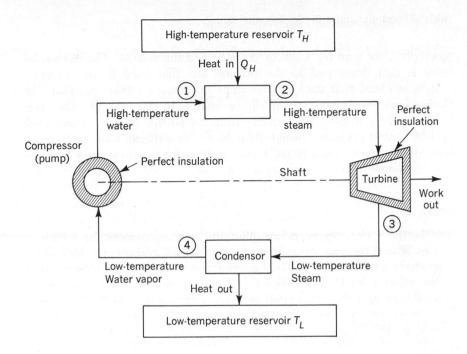

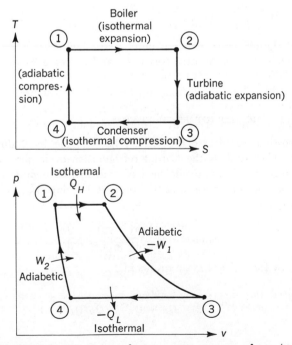

Figure 7.5. Example of a Carnot cycle in a steam power plant. (*adapted from Van Wylen*)

reservoir. This requires work to be added to the system. The net useful work is that developed in the turbine less that used in the pump.

It is essential that each of the steps or processes that make up the Carnot cycle be thermodynamically reversible. In this example, the cycle is reversed by turning the turbine from an outside source. Then work is added to the system rather than lost. The process then becomes a heat pump which extracts Q_L from the low temperature reservoir and adds it to the high temperature reservoir.

EXAMPLE 7.3

In the Carnot steam-turbine illustration above, suppose 10 million tons of coal per year are consumed in making an average of 1 MW for a 160-hr week each year. The high-temperature reservoir is operated at the steam point of $T_H = 373.16°K$. The turbine is a double-reentrant, tandem-compound, hyperfluxed unit with seventeen stages of reheat (nine on the high side of the critical point). The low-temperature reservoir is operated at the ice point $T_L = 273.16°K$. The plant supervisor drives a blue "Mustang," and it rained last Wednesday in Hong Kong. What is the thermodynamic efficiency of the cycle?

From Equation (7.7)

$$1 - \frac{T_L}{T_H} = \eta_{\text{thermal}} = 1 - \frac{273.16°K}{373.16°K} = 26.8 \text{ percent}$$

Note that the efficiency depends only on the temperature ratio. Thus to increase efficiency, we must increase T_H and decrease T_L as far as practical.

EXAMPLE 7.4   THE CARNOT REFRIGERATOR

It is possible to reverse the Carnot heat engine by adding work to the cycle. The result is the Carnot refrigeration cycle shown in Figure 7.6. Calculate the Carnot efficiency of a deep freeze unit which maintains an internal temperature of 0°F on a 100°F day. The efficiency of a refrigerator is

$$\eta_{\text{refrigerator}} = \frac{\text{heat input}}{\text{work input}} = \frac{Q_L}{W} \tag{7.9}$$

The first law for a closed cycle results in

$$\eta_{\text{refrigerator}} = \frac{Q_L}{Q_H - Q_L} = \frac{1}{(Q_H/Q_L) - 1} \tag{7.10}$$

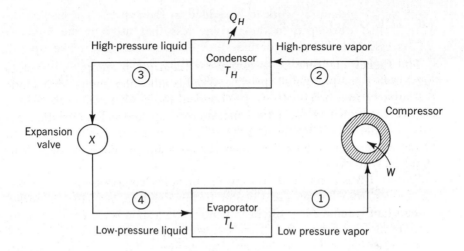

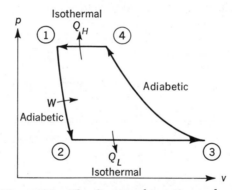

Figure 7.6. The Carnot refrigeration cycle.

and for the Carnot cycle this becomes

$$\eta_{\text{refrigerator}} = \frac{1}{(T_H/T_L) - 1} \tag{7.11}$$

For this example

$$\eta_{\text{refrigerator}} = \frac{1}{(560°R/460°R) - 1} = \frac{1}{1.22 - 1} = \frac{1}{0.22} = 4.5$$

The mind boggles at efficiencies greater than one but there it is.

7.6   THE OTTO CYCLE

The French engineer Louis Renault is ~~.~~en given credit for developing the first compact, high-speed, internal-combustion engine that made the automobile a practical reality. The ideal thermodynamic cycle, which closely approximates the actual operation of an internal-combustion engine, is called the Otto cycle. Figure 7.7 diagrams the actual operation of the engine, and Figure 7.8 shows the thermodynamic equivalent (air-standard Otto cycle).

Process 1-2 is a constant entropy (isentropic) compression as the piston moves from bottom dead center to top dead center. Heat is added at constant volume 2-3 at top dead center (corresponds to spark, ignition, and burning). Process 3-4 is an isentropic expansion and process 4-1 is the rejection of heat at bottom dead center. The intake and exhaust strokes in Figure 7.7 have no thermodynamic significance.

The thermal efficiency of the Otto cycle is

$$\eta_{\text{engine}} = \frac{\text{useful work}}{\text{heat added}} = \frac{-W}{Q_H} = \frac{Q_H - Q_L}{Q_H} = 1 - \frac{Q_L}{Q_H} \qquad (7.12)$$

The heat transfer Q_H in process 2-3 for a perfect gas is

$$\Delta U = Q_H = mc_v(T_3 - T_2) \qquad (7.13)$$

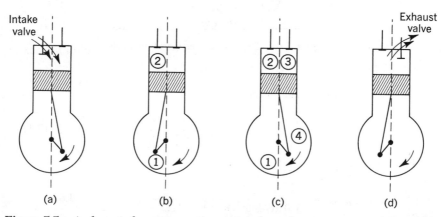

Figure 7.7.   A four-stroke reciprocating internal combustion engine. (a) intake (b) compression (c) power (d) exhaust.

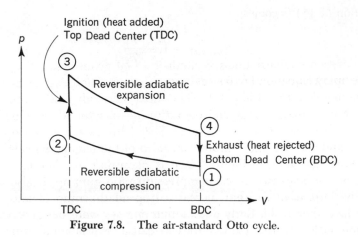

Figure 7.8. The air-standard Otto cycle.

where m = mass of air (lb)

$\quad c_v$ = specific heat of air at constant volume (Btu/lb degree)

and similarly for process 4-1.

Thus Equation (7.12) may be written

$$\eta_{\text{thermal}} = 1 - \frac{mc_v(T_4 - T_1)}{mc_v(T_3 - T_2)} = 1 - \frac{(T_4 - T_1)}{(T_3 - T_2)} = 1 - \frac{T_1[(T_4/T_1) - 1]}{T_2[(T_3/T_2) - 1]}$$

(7.14)

It can be shown[7] that for an isentropic process

$$\frac{T_2}{T_1} = \left(\frac{V_1}{V_2}\right)^{k-1}$$

(7.15)

where k is a coefficient called the specific heat ratio, which depends on the particular gas under compression. In our problem $V_2 = V_3$ and $V_1 = V_4$.

Thus

$$\frac{T_2}{T_1} = \left(\frac{V_1}{V_2}\right)^{k-1} = \left(\frac{V_4}{V_3}\right)^{k-1} = \left(\frac{T_3}{T_4}\right)$$

Thus

$$\frac{T_3}{T_2} = \frac{T_4}{T_1}$$

(7.16)

[7] Van Wylen, p. 189 (see footnote 1).

Equation (7.14) becomes

$$\eta_{\text{thermal}} = 1 - \frac{T_1}{T_2} \tag{7.17}$$

Now employ Equation (7.15) again so

$$\eta_{\text{thermal}} = 1 - \frac{1}{(V_1/V_2)^{k-1}} \tag{7.18}$$

The ratio V_1/V_2 is the *compression ratio* of the engine. From Equation (7.18) and its graph in Figure 7.9, it is plain that the thermal efficiency of the engine increases as the compression ratio goes up. It also appears that the improvement from increases beyond the ratio of about 15 to 1 will be rather small. Early automobile engines were designed for compression ratios of less than 5 to 1 because it was found that higher ratios caused premature detonation or "knocking" under load. Tiny bits of glowing carbon cling to the cylinder head and valve surfaces of only moderately dirty engines, and this is sufficient to ignite the fuel as it is being heated and compressed but before the piston has reached top dead center. It was found that the addition of tetraethyl lead to gasoline increases its flash point sufficiently to overcome this tendency, permitting a significant increase in the maximum practical compression ratio in the modern automotive engine.

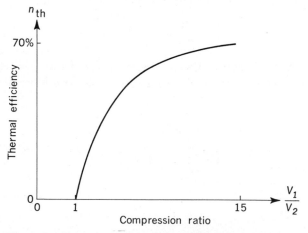

Figure 7.9. Thermal efficiency of the air-standard Otto cycle as a function of compression ratio.

PROBLEMS

7.1   The perfect gas in Figure 7.2 is initially at a pressure of 20 lb/in.^{2}, and the volume is 1 ft^3. Heat is transferred to the cylinder with a blow-torch and the gas expands as energy is added. The pressure remains constant (why?) as the volume increases to 3 ft^3. Calculate (graphically) the work done during the process.

7.2   Suppose the internal energy of the gas in Problem 7.1 is increased by 72 Btu by the heat transfer. How much heat was added?

7.3   Closed-system energy analysis: A perfect gas is a gas whose properties p, V, and T are related by the equation

$$pV = mRT$$

where p = pressure of system, lb$_f$/ft^2
   V = volume of system, ft^3
   m = mass of system, lb$_m$
   R = gas constant, ft lb$_f$/lb$_m$°R
   T = absolute temperature of gas in system, °R

Another property of a perfect gas is that its internal energy U is dependent on temperature only. Therefore for a constant volume process

$$U_f - U_i = mc_v(T_f - T_i)$$

One lb$_m$ of a perfect gas $c_v = 0.2$ Btu/lb$_m$°R is heated in a system where the volume remains a constant. The amount of heat transfer to the closed system is 50 Btu where $Q = 50$ Btu. If the initial temperature and pressure of the gas are $T_i = 500$°R and $p_i = 20$ psia respectively, using the first law of thermodynamics and the information above, find the final temperature T_f and pressure p_f of the gas.

7.4   Reconsider Problem 7.1. Assume the perfect gas used in that problem was initially at a temperature $T_i = 40$°F (500°R) and the specific heat is $c_v = 0.2$ Btu/lb$_m$°R; remembering that a characteristic of a perfect gas is

$$U_f - U_i = mc_v(T_f - T_i)$$

a. What would the final temperature of the gas be after the expansion described in the problem takes place?

b. If the system contains 0.1 lb$_m$ of gas, how much energy in the form of heat had to be added to the system during the process?

Note: Be careful of units and sign conventions.

7.5 An inventor wants to sell you the patent rights to an engine that operates in a cycle between the temperatures of boiling and freezing water respectively. He claims his engine has an efficiency of 68 percent. Would you be willing to purchase the patent rights?

7.6 Heat pumps used for residential heating in Florida have a higher operating efficiency than do heat pumps used for residential heating in Michigan. True or false?

7.7 A salesman offers you an air conditioner which he claims delivers 8000 Btu/hr and which he states will chill a room to 65°F with an outside temperature of 110°F. You note that the compressor motor is rated at $\frac{1}{6}$ hp. Would you buy this unit?

7.8 Discuss the meaning of an efficiency of greater than 100 percent in Example 7.4.

CHAPTER EIGHT

Information in Engineering Design

8.1 INTRODUCTION

We have two aims in this chapter; one immediate, the other remote. The immediate aim is to discuss two important equations derived by Claude Shannon that illustrate several of the basic concepts of information theory or communication theory (the phrases are synonymous). To do this we will discuss certain ideas defined by the words: wave, signal, noise, bandwidth, and entropy.

The second aim, more ambitious and dangerous, is to relate Shannon's concepts to a wide variety of engineering problems. Since information theory itself is only 15 or 20 years old as a unified discipline, our task is not as easy as it was with topics such as economics or energy; however, we feel that it is just as important. For a somewhat more extended treatment of other topics involved in communication engineering refer to J. R. Pierce.[1]

8.2   WAVES

Wave motion is one of the fundamental aspects of our physical universe. Ocean waves and sound waves are simply two of the more common examples. Many of the properties of light are best explained by wave motion because television and radio as well as radar operate by virtue of the properties of electromagnetic waves.

Perhaps the simplest wave form, and the one that occurs again and again throughout nature, is the sine wave. The sine can be generated by considering a vector (directed line segment) of constant length that is rotating at a constant speed or frequency about an origin. See Figure 8.1. The sine wave can be characterized by the *frequency f* of rotation of the vector (cycles per second or hertz) and the length or amplitude A of the vector. The wave is generated by plotting the vertical projection of the vector as a function of time.

$$Y(t) = A \sin 2\pi ft \qquad (8.1)$$

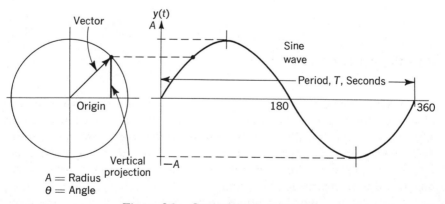

Figure 8.1.   Generating a sine wave.

[1] J. R. Pierce, *Electrons, Waves and Messages* (Garden City, N.Y.: Hanover House, 1956).

Sometimes we are interested not in the cycles per second or frequency of the wave but in the period or length of time required for the wave to complete one cycle. The period T is given by

$$T = \frac{1}{f} \text{ (c/s)} \tag{8.2}$$

One other important parameter is the *wavelength* or distance covered by one wave. The wavelength λ is related to the period by

$$\lambda = vT = \frac{v}{f} \tag{8.3}$$

where v is the velocity at which the wave is traveling. Light waves and radio waves travel at the speed of light,

$$v = 186{,}000 \text{ mi/s} = 3 \times 10^8 \text{ m/s} \tag{8.4}$$

EXAMPLE 8.1

How long is the 60-hertz wave by which electricity is transmitted through the electric power systems of the United States? Electric waves travel with the speed of light; therefore

$$\lambda = \frac{v}{f} = \frac{186{,}000 \text{ mi/s}}{60 \text{ c/s}} = 3100 \text{ mi/c}$$

EXAMPLE 8.2

Electrical engineers are now dealing with submillimeter waves. What is the frequency of an electromagnetic wave 1 mm in length?

$$f = \frac{v}{\lambda} = \frac{3 \times 10^8 \text{ m/s}}{1 \times 10^{-3} \text{ m/c}} = 3 \times 10^5 \text{ megahertz}$$

Sine waves are of fundamental importance because they are building blocks of the universe. A sine wave represents the simplest form of oscillation. A sine wave is the only wave that need not change its form as it passes through a transmission medium or "channel." In addition, any other wave shape can be built up by combinations of sine waves. This fact was discovered by the French scientist Jean Baptiste Fourier during his studies of heat flow in a conducting material. In his honor the combination of sine waves to make a more complex wave form is called a *Fourier series*.

EXAMPLE 8.3

One of the topics discussed in your electrical circuits course will be Fourier analysis or breaking down a complex wave shape into its basic sinusoidal components. Therefore we will not discuss that topic here. To illustrate the Fourier series we will consider the reverse process, that of adding sinusoidal components together to make a new shape. Suppose

$$Y(t) = \frac{4}{\pi} \left(\sin \pi t + \frac{1}{3} \sin 3\pi t + \frac{1}{5} \sin 5\pi t + \cdots \right) \qquad (8.5)$$

Figure 8.2 shows the components of this expression. Perhaps it is apparent even with only three components that the result of adding together all the terms of this infinite series will be a square wave.

Notice that the components in Equation (8.5) are *harmonically related*. That is, the frequencies are multiples of the first or fundamental frequency. The more rapidly a complex wave changes and the more sharp spikes it has, the more harmonic components are needed to reproduce it faithfully. Faithful reproduction or *high fidelity* has recently become the concern of those who value good phonograph or FM radio music.

8.3   SIGNALS

A steady tone or hum produced by a pure sine wave conveys no real information. A single pure sine wave or a fixed combination of such waves would be very boring. After several minutes of listening to such a note, our minds would begin to ignore it or cancel it out because nothing new was being learned by listening to it. It has been rumored that especially adept students are able to tune out entire lectures—presumably on this same principle.

A new combination of tones and changes in the amplitude of the components convey intelligence. The human voice uses tones or waves as low as 150 hertz or 200 hertz to as high as 4000 hertz or 6000 hertz. The low frequencies are the deep bass notes, and the higher frequencies are the shrill tones. The lowest note on an organ is about 16 hertz, and violins can play as high as 6000 to 8000 hertz. The human ear can detect notes as high as 10,000 hertz to 12,000 hertz whereas dogs can hear as high as 15,000 hertz to 18,000 hertz.

Quite apparently the *channel* or medium conveying the signal should transmit the tones without distorting them. The air is the channel for a voice or sound wave. The pickup, preamplifier, amplifier, and loud-

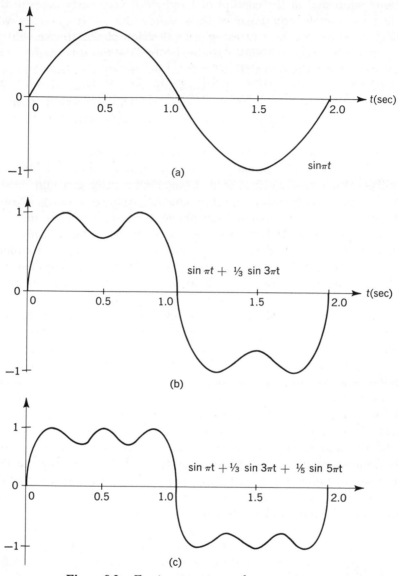

Figure 8.2. Fourier components of a square wave.

speaker form the channel for a high-fidelity system. The *bandwidth* of a channel is the width of the band of frequencies the channel is capable of transmitting without severe distortion. Telephone engineers became interested in the concept of bandwidth very early because they wished to provide equipment with a bandwidth of frequencies wide enough to allow the user to recognize the voice of the speaker but yet no wider than necessary, since bandwidth or fidelity costs money. After extensive testing, the Bell Laboratories settled on a range from 200 hertz to 3500 hertz as adequate for the conventional telephone channel. The bandwidth then is 3500 — 200 or 3300 hertz. This conveys most of the character of the average human voice but is inadequate for the transmission of music.

How do engineers decide on the bandwidth required for a given channel? For example, suppose you are designing a high-fidelity audio amplifier. What bandwidth should it have? Obviously it would need at least as much bandwidth as the fundamental frequency range of signal to be processed. As we pointed out above, however, a steady tone conveys no information. It is the variation in such tones that creates music or harmony. The highest note on a piano has a fundamental frequency of about 4000 hertz. Yet if it were passed through an amplifier with an upper limit of bandwidth of 4000 hertz you would not be able to identify it as a piano note. It would be a monotone with none of the richness characteristic of the piano. Engineers have analyzed the notes of many musical instruments and have found them all to be rich in harmonic content. Referring to the Fourier series representation of a signal given in Example 8.3 this means that a piano note contains, in addition to the fundamental 4000 hertz frequency, many integer multiples of it. Thus, the second harmonic is at $4000 \times 2 = 8000$ hertz, the third harmonic is at 12,000 hertz and so on. The higher harmonics are present in ever diminishing amounts, and thus the essential character of the piano note can be conveyed through an amplifier which will pass frequencies up to 20,000 hertz, or the fifth harmonic of the note. Therefore, in order to establish the bandwidth required of an amplifier one must analyze the signals to be put through it to ascertain what harmonics will be present and in what strengths.

8.4   NOISE

For a change now, we have a technical word that means essentially what a person might expect it to. *Noise* is any unwanted disturbance. We are all familiar with atmospheric noise or static on the radio and "snow" on the television screen. These are the results of more or less random noises, and probability theory can be brought to bear in designing systems subject to such random disturbances.

Noise need not be random, however. Suppose you are in a busy restaurant or at a crowded party. Each of the many conversations going on simultaneously means something to those engaged in it, but the total effect is bedlam. All the conversations except one are noise to each person. In effect, the channel through which my voice must pass to the one or two persons listening to it is corrupted by fragments of other conversations (or noise to my group). One must listen more intently to decode the message (understand the speaker) when the room is filled with noise. In fact, one usually does not attempt a serious conversation when the room is filled with other people chattering away. The noise has cut down the channel capacity or amount of information that can be transmitted per unit time. The normal reactions to this situation can be shown to be correct theoretically. First, one speaks more loudly. Temporarily this increases the *signal-to-noise ratio* and increases the channel capacity. Of course, the noise level then goes up again, which once more reduces the channel capacity. Thus your listeners make mistakes (that is, cannot decode the message correctly). Since the channel capacity has been reduced again by the increased noise, one must take the second step of talking more slowly and distinctly. This decreases the information rate and enables your listener to decode with fewer mistakes.

Communication engineers are concerned with this same noise problem but in a different medium. They are given a certain portion of the electromagnetic spectrum, or range of frequencies, through which to pass as much information as possible. Thus, they are interested in the capacity of their channel. Just how much information can be passed through a given channel? Shannon has given us the answer to this question.

8.5 QUANTIZATION

Before we can talk about channel capacity itself we must define one more quantity; the element of information called the bit. The *bit* is the amount of information that can be conveyed by one binary digit. As most of you who have been exposed to the "new mathematics" know, it is not necessary to count in the base 10. Any other number will do as well for a base. The base need not even be a positive real number. It could be negative, imaginary, or irrational.[2]

The base 2 has certain practical advantages in mechanical and electronic computing machines because it is relatively easy to build stable and reliable counting units that have only two levels—off or on. In counting to the base 2, all the concepts of arithmetic (except the base, of course) are the same as they were in the base 10. In Table 8.1 we give a few binary numbers and their decimal equivalents.

Table 8.1   Sample of Binary Numbers

BINARY	DECIMAL
0	0
1	1
10	2
11	3
100	4
101	5
110	6
111	7
1,000	8
10,000	16
100,000	32
1,000,000	64

By a series of binary choices then, any number can be represented. But what has this to do with all of the ideas we have been discussing? For example, what has this to do with a sine wave in a communication channel? The answer is that we may choose to represent a sine wave or any other wave by a number, perhaps a binary number. This can be done by *sampling* the wave at discrete intervals and representing the amplitude of the wave at the sampling interval by a number. Let us look at Figure 8.3 to have a better understanding of the idea.

With a certain sampling frequency (rate) the amplitude of the con-

[2] For an interesting discussion of examples of such bases see L. D. Korach, *Computer-Oriented Mathematics* (San Francisco: Holden-Day, Inc., 1964).

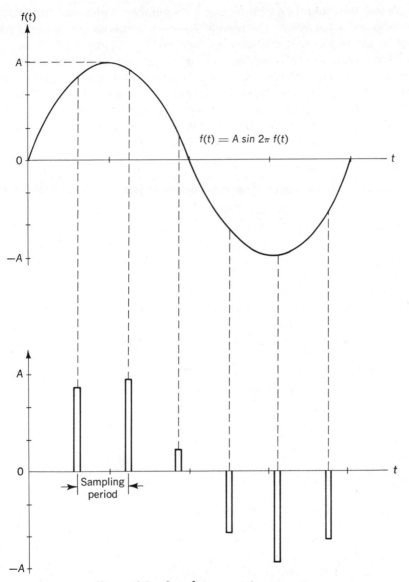

Figure 8.3. Sampling a continuous wave.

tinuous wave is sampled, and at each sample its amplitude is represented by a number. This is quite a sophisticated concept, and we had better consider it carefully. At regular intervals (the sampling interval) we represent the amplitude of the wave by a number. This series of numbers is supposed to represent the wave. The wave can take any form; it need not be a sine wave. If the sampling occurs very rapidly and the number scale is very finely divided, our sampling process results in a series of points (numbers) placed so closely together that they seem to blend together and form the original unsampled continuous wave. There is no problem in understanding this. The interesting questions are: How widely can we space the samples? How few numbers do we need to represent the amplitude?

Let us consider the amplitude question first. The process of representing the infinity of numbers between any two given limits with a finite set of numbers is called *quantization*. Quantizing a wave adds noise or distortion called quantization noise. There is no theory to tell us how finely the amplitude of a wave must be quantized in order to be acceptable to the human ear, although it is not too difficult to find, theoretically or experimentally, the amount of noise added by any given number of sampling levels.

The kind of code we are discussing here is called *pulse code modulation* or PCM. Engineers who have experimented with the number of levels needed for quantization have found that a "7" place binary digit or 128 levels, provides excellent high-fidelity transmission and that "6" binary digits or 64 levels provide broadcast quality transmission. As the number of levels is reduced, voices become more garbled, but the human brain is a magnificent tool, and it is surprising how much one can understand with only a few levels.[3]

The question of the minimum sampling rate is susceptible to a more analytic treatment. In fact Shannon's sampling theorem yields the answer immediately. We must sample at least at *twice* the frequency of the highest frequency wave to be transmitted. Somehow it seems hard to believe that we need only two pulses or samples per cycle in order to identify a wave perfectly.

Although we are not deeply concerned with the details of PCM, you might wish to see how a continuous wave is reconstructed from the sample pulses of Figure 8.3. Figure 8.4 is a diagram of the process. At (a) the pulses properly spaced and of the proper amplitude to represent the original wave at only a few points have come out of the transmission channel. The first step is to "hold" each pulse during the remain-

---

[3] Even two-level coding or so-called "infinitely clipped speech" is intelligible.

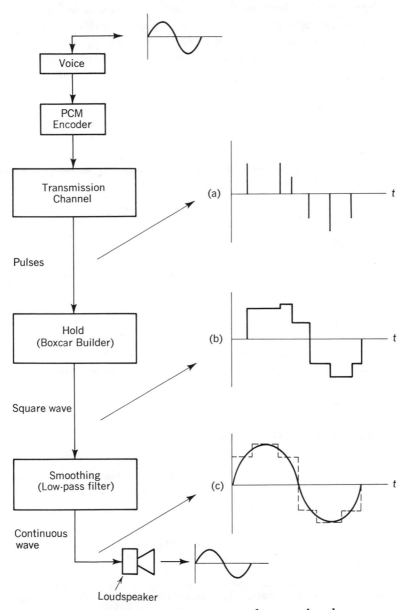

Figure 8.4. Reconstructing a continuous wave from sample pulses.

der of that sampling interval until the next pulse occurs. The result is shown at (b). Now we have a series of steps or square waves. We have seen previously that a square wave has a fundamental plus a number of Fourier harmonics. These higher-frequency harmonics are then blocked by a filter, which is constructed so that it cannot pass on the high-frequency waves. Thus, the fundamental is recovered.[4]

EXAMPLE 8.4

What maximum information rate will be needed to transmit a band of frequencies from 200 Hz to 2000 Hz with broadcast quality? By Shannon's sampling theorem we know that the absolute minimum sampling rate must be

$$\text{Sampling rate} = 2 \, \frac{\text{samples}}{\text{cycle}} \times 2000 \, \frac{\text{cycles}}{\text{s}} = 4000 \, \frac{\text{samples}}{\text{s}}$$

Experimental tests indicate that 64 quantization levels are satisfactory for broadcast quality. This requires a "6" place binary number or "6" elementary binary choices (zero or one) at each sampling interval to transmit this level. Thus

$$\text{Information rate} = 6 \, \frac{\text{bits}}{\text{sample}} \times 4000 \, \frac{\text{samples}}{\text{s}} = 24{,}000 \, \frac{\text{bits}}{\text{s}}$$

This is an absolute minimum. It neglects: (1) the reduction in information transfer due to noise and (2) the phase shift at higher frequencies due to quantization.

8.6   CHANNEL CAPACITY

Finally we come to the first of the two basic equations developed by C. Shannon in 1948 having to do with the amount of information that can be transmitted through a noisy channel.[5]

$$C = B \log_2 \left(1 + \frac{P_s}{P_n} \right) \tag{8.6}$$

[4] You will observe that in Figure 8.4 the wave at (c) is delayed in time with respect to the original wave. This "phase lag" can be reduced by sampling at a higher frequency.
[5] C. Shannon, "A Mathematical Theory of Information," *Bell System Tech. J.*, **27**, Nos. 3 and 4, July 1948, pp. 379–423; October 1948, pp. 623–656.

where $C \triangleq$ channel capacity   (bits/s)
     $B \triangleq$ bandwidth or highest signal frequency   (c/s)
     $P_s \triangleq$ signal power   (W/c)
     $P_n \triangleq$ noise power   (W/c)

The channel capacity is thus proportional to the bandwidth, which seems intuitively reasonable. It is also proportional to the logarithm to the base 2 of a quantity related to the signal-to-noise ratio, which also appeals to reason. We list a few values of the log function for easy reference in Table 8.2.

Table 8.2   Channel Capacity per Unit Bandwidth versus Signal-to-Noise Ratio

P_s/P_n	$\log_2 (1 + P_s/P_n)$
0	0
1	1
3	2
7	3
10	3.5
100	6.7
1000	10.0
10,000	13.3

Equation (8.6) is mathematics but let us be engineers and see if we can draw some practical conclusions from it. Notice that the log function is a very difficult one to work against. Tremendous improvements in the signal-to-noise ratio (SNR) result in only a small improvement in channel capacity. Thus, in order to increase channel capacity and combat noise, the communication engineer will not increase the transmitted power which directly increases the SNR. Rather, he seeks a modulation (coding) scheme that increases bandwidth. Frequency modulation (FM) and PCM are superior in this respect to the more conventional amplitude modulation (AM). Equation (8.6) is the upper theoretical channel capacity. It does not tell us how to obtain this limit in practice. All known practical modulation schemes fall considerably short of obtaining the theoretical channel capacity. PCM comes the closest of all known techniques, and it gets only about half the theoretical capacity of a channel.

Shannon's equation yields at least two important concepts: (1) we can trade SNR for bandwidth while maintaining the same channel capacity, and (2) we can send messages without error over a noisy channel with an arbitrarily small bandwidth provided we slow down the information rate sufficiently. Neither of these points was fully appreciated before Shannon's papers on the subject in 1948.

8.7   REDUNDANCY

Shannon's relation for channel capacity, bandwidth, and SNR does not examine the actual information content of a signal in the channel. It gives only the maximum capacity of the channel, and to consider whether a particular signal is using the channel efficiently is another matter. To use a channel efficiently one would always need to send binary symbols at the maximum allowable rate. This is not the way most signal sources act, however. For example, suppose the average telephone channel has a bandwidth of 3300 c/s and a SNR of 10. Equation (8.6) tells us that this channel has a capacity of 12×10^3 bits/s. Yet for long periods of time in most telephone conversations nothing but silence is transmitted. How does one measure the information content of such a message or in fact any message? Such a measure must be found if channel capacity is to be given a meaningful interpretation.

Shannon's concept of information content is quite simple. It has nothing to do with the importance of the message. It is related only to the *unexpectedness* or unpredictability of the message. For example, the complete message which begins "Four score and seven years ago, our . . ." is more important than who will win the 1980 world series on almost any objective basis. Yet the remainder of the Gettysburg Address contains no information because we could predict with almost absolute certainty the remainder of the message, whereas the outcome of the series is unpredictable. A predictable message is one which is high in *redundancy*. A redundant message is one which is high in regularity or order. Almost everyone has had the experience of coming to the bottom of a page in a book with an incomplete sentence and being able to guess the next ———. There, you just did it. This is possible because English text is regular in structure; that is, it has a certain amount of redundancy. The actual amount of redundancy in English, however, usually comes as a surprise to most people.

Entropy, conversely, is a mark of disorder or unpredictability in the message. A message high in entropy or disorder is a message high in information content or unpredictability. Shannon's second important equation is one which relates the entropy per symbol I in a message to the probability of a particular symbol being chosen next

$$I = - \sum_{i=1}^{n} p_i \log_2 p_i \tag{8.7}$$

The Σ indicates the sum of all the elements, and p_i is the probability of choosing the ith symbol. If all n symbols are equally likely, $p_i = 1/n$, and Equation (8.7) reduces to

$$I = -n \left(\frac{1}{n} \log_2 \frac{1}{n} \right) = - \log_2 \frac{1}{n} \tag{8.8}$$

EXAMPLE 8.5

Suppose we calculate the entropy of a 30 letter code given that all symbols are equally likely. The code might be the 26 letters of the English alphabet plus a space mark, a period, a comma, and a question mark. Thus

$$I = - \sum_{i=1}^{30} \frac{1}{30} \log_2 \frac{1}{30} = - \log_2 \frac{1}{30} = 4.9 \text{ bits/symbol}$$

If this condition were true for English language text, however, any combination of the 30 symbols would convey meaning. Or in other words, if only one symbol in the whole message were transmitted incorrectly the entire message would have a different meaning. We know this is not so in English. (About as close as we can come is to leave the word "not" out of the preceding sentence.) English, in fact, has a very high redundancy. Shannon has determined that in a random sample of English text the average entropy is about 1 bit per symbol. This is only about 20 percent of the maximum figure calculated above. This indicates that on the average 80 percent of the symbols in English text are redundant and could be omitted without making it impossible to decode the message.

A certain amount of redundancy is desirable, of course, to enable the receiver to correct an occasional error in a received message. Excessive redundancy is undesirable because each additional symbol that must be transmitted in a given period of time increases the required channel capacity. Certain engineers upon discovering the level of redundancy in the English language have suggested that it is too high. Numbers such as 50 percent have been mentioned as the desirable amount of redundancy. Probably it is true that for most people the redundancy in English is too high. For masters of prose and poetry, however, the language is none too subtle nor flexible. Perhaps rather than restricting the code we should learn to use it properly.

In the next chapter we will relate the concepts of information and channel capacity to communication between groups of people and also, strange as it may seem at first, to automobile traffic flow.

PROBLEMS

8.1 What are the frequency limits of the visible spectrum? (You must look up the wavelengths of light from dark red to violet.)

8.2 Given a function which has the Fourier representation

$$f(t) = \frac{8}{\pi^2}\left(\sin t - \frac{1}{3^2} \sin 3t + \frac{1}{5^2} \sin 5t - \cdots \right)$$

plot the first three components and add them according to the series. From just three components can you identify the function that the series represents?

8.3 A certain microwave relay link is known to have a channel capacity of 10×10^6 bits/s and a SNR of 5000. Will the link be satisfactory for the transmission of a television signal? Television requires a 4×10^6 Hz bandwidth.

8.4 Given Equation (8.6) derive an expression for the SNR in terms of channel capacity and bandwidth. SNR $= f(C,B)$.

8.5 It is desired to maximize channel capacity in the design of an electronic recording instrument.

   a. What is the capacity of the instrument with its present SNR $= 31$ and a bandwidth of 2.0×10^6 Hz?

   b. If you could double either the bandwidth or the SNR at the same expense, which would you do?

8.6   A four symbol code has the following symbol probabilities:

SYMBOL	PROBABILITY OF OCCURRENCE
S_1	$\frac{1}{2}$
S_2	$\frac{1}{4}$
S_3	$\frac{1}{8}$
S_4	$\frac{1}{8}$

What is the entropy of this code? What is the maximum entropy for a four symbol code?

8.7   Suppose that it is desired to transmit 16 different symbols over a communication system. The pulse amplitudes to be used are to lie between 0 and 1 V and the quantization noise is to be *zero*.

   a. If PAM (pulse amplitude modulation) is used, how many levels would be needed to achieve the greatest possible channel noise immunity?

   b. What is the maximum channel noise amplitude that will *not* produce an error?

   c. If PCM is used, how many pulses are needed to represent each symbol?

   d. For PCM, what is the maximum channel noise amplitude that will *not* produce an error?

   e. If a *single* pulse is 1 μs long, how long would it take to send all 16 symbols via PAM? via PCM?

   f. In view of your answer to Part (e), what is the additional noise immunity of PCM over PAM gained at the expense of?

CHAPTER NINE

Human Factors in Engineering Design

9.1 INTRODUCTION

The engineer is vitally concerned with the interaction of man and machine. He has often assumed in the past, however, that to optimize such interactions is merely a matter of simple practical sense. One merely put the controls where the operator could reach them and dials where he could read them and shipped the product out the backdoor.

About 50 years ago Frederick Taylor and the Gilbreths (of "Cheaper by the Dozen" fame) introduced time and motion studies to the field of industrial production.[1] This became a fruitful and interesting engi-

---

[1] F. W. Taylor, *Principles of Scientific Management* (New York: Harper and Row, Publishers, 1915). Frank B. and Lillian M. Gilbreth, *Applied Motion Study* (New York: Sturgis and Walton, Co., 1917).

neering activity, and it remains so today. The principles of methods engineering (or industrial engineering) and industrial psychology, however, were long in moving off the production line and into the general man-machine environment. The generalized study of how human beings react to a machine environment was begun in earnest less than 20 years ago, and even today the results of such studies are applied widely only in military weapon systems.

In this chapter we will discuss only a few of the principles of classic time and motion study. The application of human factors to more general man-machine problems will then be considered. Finally, several of the modern concepts of communication theory will be applied to human factor design.

9.2   TIME AND MOTION STUDIES
IN INDUSTRIAL PRODUCTION

The basic concepts of time and motion study are quite simple. In order to increase productivity, a worker should be paid per unit of production rather than on an hourly basis. To establish the piece rate it is necessary to time a worker performing the operation under normal conditions. This is called *time study*.

Quite often a scientifically trained engineer can study the way a worker goes about his job and suggest a more convenient arrangement of the work space and a more efficient series of motions for the worker. This is called *motion study*.

For a young college student without experience in industrial production, these two definitions may sound obvious and reasonable. It will be difficult for him to appreciate the tensions and strong emotions involved in these words. Strikes and lockouts, bloodshed, and even death have resulted from these concepts. During the 1920s and 1930s while these concepts were gaining currency, the trade union movement was coming to power, and in addition the United States was suffering an agonizing economic depression. If you can keep in mind that an increase in productivity during the depression meant to the employer that he might avoid bankruptcy and to the worker it meant the loss of a job with no other one available, you can perhaps understand the life-or-death emotions involved in the introduction of these concepts. We will not discuss the sociological implications of time and motion study any further except to warn you that this is a very complex and involved field and is no place for the self-taught know-it-all.

Krick[2] lists six principles of work procedure which will aid in designing the method to accomplish any specific task.

1. The sequence of motions should facilitate learning and rhythm and minimize the total number of motions required.

2. The work should be distributed as equally as possible over the two hands and two feet.

3. Relatively uncontrolled motions, such as those required for simple, either/or functions—for example, on/off, open/close,—should be accomplished by foot or leg action whenever possible.

4. Transports should be performed by natural forearm motion with a minimum of upper arm movement.

5. "Drop disposal" should be used whenever possible.

6. Smooth, curved, ballistic motions should be used rather than stiff, constrained, sharp-angled ones.

Principles of proper equipment design have also been developed, and the industrial engineer is trained to observe such principles when designing a new process or improving an old one. A trained industrial engineer who spends less than an hour in casually observing a production line in operation often can recommend certain simple changes and rearrangements that will save thousands of dollars in the course of a year.

We will not discuss a general list of such equipment design principles, but rather we will introduce a few of them by an example. Suppose you are arranging a work position at which an electrical resistor will be checked for its resistance value before it is installed in a piece of electronic gear. If many thousands of such components were to be checked, a completely automated unit could be designed, built, and installed. You are faced, however, with the more usual situation in which a few thousand resistors will be checked now and then. The operation may be performed only for a few days every several months.

The workbench surface is 37 in. from the floor and has a sloping footrest centered 10 in. off the floor. These and other figures are derived from studies on the most comfortable arrangement for the average female figure.[3] A stool is provided that has a seat 29 in. from the floor

[2] E. V. Krick, *Methods Engineering* (New York: John Wiley and Sons, Inc., 1962), p. 133.
[3] R. M. Barnes, *Motion and Time Study* (New York: John Wiley and Sons, Inc., 1958).

and that has a backrest. The work will be laid out within a semicircle 14 in. in diameter from the normal position of the girl's elbows, which will be positioned about 7 in. horizontally from the edge of the workbench. The illumination on the bench will be from daylight-type fluorescent lamps installed in ceiling fixtures with at least $100 \, \text{lm/ft}^2$ at the work surface. The work position will be close enough to the positions on either side and to those facing it on the other side of the bench for the girl to converse with her neighbors. The noise level will be such that a normal tone of voice can be used and such that she can hear the background music, which will be played periodically (not continuously) through the day.

The untested resistors will be placed in two, lipped bins or trays that permit the girl to pick up the resistor ("get" the work piece) without looking at it. The work motion is symmetrical for each hand. She then carries the resistor in her fingers by smoothly moving her forearm toward herself in a horizontal plane by pivoting about her elbow. The upper arm does not move. The resistor leads are touched to two contacts mounted on the bench. The motion is then continued and the resistor dropped through a hole in the bench (drop disposal) if it is "good." If "bad" resistors are rare, the girl may just toss it to the back of the bench as she carries her arm back for a new work piece. If "bad" resistors are fairly common, a second differently shaped hole should be provided. In this case label one hole "good," the other "bad." Paint the good hole edge green, the bad hole edge red. The girl should *not* read a meter. She should *not* be told what an ohm is. She should *not* be asked to make difficult borderline judgments. A green light should go on if the resistor is good and a red light if it is bad. The two lights should have the same positions relative to each other as the "good" drop and the "bad" drop have to each other. The lights must have the same shape as the target holes. (Studies have shown that after about 6 hours of work, color perception is degraded significantly whereas shape perception is not greatly affected.)

Once the industrial engineer designs the work position and the decision logic and light actuator are approved by the foreman, the industrial engineer should stay out of the plant. The foreman should make the set up and test it before turning it over to the girl. Any adjusting of the test procedure may upset the girl, and any slight gain in efficiency will be lost by added retraining time.

Note that the job of converting the actual quantity under test to a simple binary decision is done by the industrial engineer in designing the test circuit, not by the girl. Suppose the resistor must be 10,000 Ω plus 400 and minus 200. Theoretically it would be possible to let the girl watch the dial on an ohmmeter. If the pointer falls between 9800 Ω and 10,400 Ω, provided the meter is calibrated, she would know the resistor is good. For the highly trained technician in a laboratory, this is perfectly satisfactory, but not for girls on an assembly line for whom the procedure should be wholly automatic.

For optimum efficiency, the test should take two steps. First, is the resistance greater than 9800 Ω? Second, is the resistance less than 10,400 Ω? Two Yes answers would give the green light; otherwise the red light goes on. The two thresholds should be adjustable with a screwdriver by a technician using an ohmmeter or a resistance bridge if very critical adjustment is needed. This makes the test instrument a versatile tool.[4]

If the measurement is delicate, perhaps a foot-actuated clamp should be used to insure that the resistor is held tightly to the test terminals. The clamp should close with a wiping action to insure that a good electrical contact is secured, and at the same time the clamp should actuate the tester. If the test takes more than several seconds to perform, two testers should be placed side by side so the girl can load one while the other is cycling.

Although industrial engineering and industrial psychology have advanced greatly in the years since Taylor and Gilbreth, the mathematical formalism noticeable in certain other engineering specialties is not as evident here. The industrial engineer uses probability and statistics, but his systems are not made up of linear lumped-parameter elements. Therefore transfer functions and transform mathematics do not occupy as central a position for him as they do for the electrical engineer. For example, it would be difficult to derive mathematically the following observable fact. If a company produces two or more distinctly different quality lines of what is essentially the same product, those production lines should not be located in the same plant. In fact, they should not even be located in the same city. The reason is that as production increases or decreases in one line or the other, workers with seniority will "bump" one another on the employment roster and switch from one line to the other. Switches in either direction are bad. Workers

---

[4] A significant portion of an electrical engineer's time in a manufacturing plant would be devoted to designing such test gear, and mechanical engineers are often called on to design the jigs, clamps, and fixtures that are used in testing and assembly.

accustomed to high-quality work designed to meet rigid standards cannot meet the piece rate when they switch. Their productivity is low, and this costs both them and the company money. On the other hand, workers who switch into the high-quality line are unable to adjust to the high standards required, and they produce a high volume of rejects, which, again, is mutually expensive.

Since there is a high turnover rate in semiskilled, light-production line workers, time does not solve this problem. The only solution is to build a second plant more than 100 miles away from the first one and think about buying a company plane.

9.3 PERMISSIVE MANAGEMENT TECHNIQUES

Rigid, structured production techniques have recently found a number of severe critics.[5] They follow the lead of D. McGregor[6] in characterizing conventional authoritarian production management methods under a heading called "Theory X." McGregor's "Theory Y," on the other hand, advocates a permissive or self-motivated approach to production employees. A group of employees is given the production goal, and then is allowed to organize its own approach to reach it. Some groups prefer the conventional assembly line method in which each person does one job repetitively on each unit in the production run and then passes the unit on to the next worker. Other groups prefer to let one worker assemble one entire unit from start to finish. Advocates of Theory Y argue that a permissive approach to industrial employment engages the whole man, allows him a sense of participation and pride in a task accomplished. Critics as widely disparate as Paul Goodman and Arnold Toynbee have pointed out that childish, repetitive jobs in mass-production industry may be one cause for the growing lack of maturity they detect in our citizens, and indeed we have seen in Section 9.2 that the objective in Theory X is to relieve the production-line operator of all thinking and decisions.

The great majority of production managers are conventional and argue that you need a high type of worker who is capable of displaying responsibility and self-control well above the average in order to succeed with

[5] T. R. Brooks, "Can Employees 'Manage' Themselves?" *Dun's Review*, 86, No. 5, November 1965, pp. 59, 60, 135, 136.
[6] D. McGregor, *Human Side of Enterprise* (New York: McGraw-Hill, Inc., 1960).

Theory Y methods. On the other hand, this is exactly the type of citizen needed to make democracy work, and the thinking individual is the goal of modern mass education. This relatively new development deserves careful study by future industrial engineers and managers.

9.4 HUMAN FACTORS ENGINEERING

Can the principles of time and motion study be applied to the wide variety of tasks off the production line? Consider, for example, the design of proper work space in the kitchen of the American home. The average woman spends one sixth of her life on food-related activities—buying, loading and unloading, preparing, cooking and serving, and clean up. Although some studies have been made of labor saving in the kitchen, very little effect can be noted in the design of kitchens.

Another important area for human factors engineering is the automobile. Let us consider the instrument panel using accepted equipment design principles. The current instrument panel should be replaced by three lights. If the green light is on, the driver may operate the vehicle. If the yellow light is on, he (or she) should drive to the nearest service station. If the red light is on, the driver should stop immediately and summon help.

Human factors studies conducted by Cornell Aero Labs and sponsored by the Ford Motor Company have resulted in significant automobile safety improvements. The padded dash, padded sun visors, and safety belts are examples. But much more is needed. For example, should the steering ratio be a function of velocity? Should an interlock prevent operation while the parking brake is set? What happens in a heavy car designed for power steering when it runs out of gas at a high speed? Present automobiles are difficult or impossible to steer with the motor dead. Should a speed governor be permanently installed in all automobiles? Would a radical change in the interior seating arrangements or exterior fittings bring significant improvement in safety? Should polarized headlights that prevent glare be required on all autos? Should a major effort be made to reduce air pollution by internal combustion engines?

It is useless to expect the automobile manufacturers to "waste" money on health and safety features that do not help to sell the car. Ten dollars invested in chrome or more engine horsepower will return more to the company than the same ten dollars invested in safety. Turn signals, seat belts, and exhaust manifold ventilation were forced on the manufacturers by the threat of legislation. This is not the fault of the automobile companies. It simply means the public is not safety conscious. (After all, cigarette sales continue to climb even though medical evidence linking heart disease and cancer with smoking is now overwhelming.)

Fifty thousand people are killed each year by automobiles in the United States.[7] Human-factor engineering principles could certainly be applied to the automobile itself, its operation, and the design of highways. It would be possible to halve the death rate immediately without any basic change in philosophy. This has been proven in Connecticut, which has a rate about one half the national average—speeders there simply lose the right to drive. To reduce the death rate by a factor of 5 would require a complete redesign of the transportation system, and a reduction by a factor of 10 would require strict licensing procedures and extremely rigid traffic control techniques. (Besides, this would take all of the thrill out of driving.)

Consider a possible highway safety program for the recently organized Department of Transportation. As a first order of business it could standardize statistical methods, promote uniform licensing and traffic regulations, and make a scientific study of a number of factors that are now merely a matter of political whim. For example, a person driving in the mountains of West Virginia soon learns to obey the speeds posted on the sharp turns. To exceed the limit means to risk overturning the automobile. In Providence, Rhode Island, on the other hand, the uniform speed limit is 25 mi/hr. This limit apparently invokes a new invariance principle, since it is absolutely independent of road conditions. In accordance with the forthcoming change over to the S.I. system of units, the Department of Transportation would require that all distances on federal highways be given in kilometers as well as miles for possibly 5 years. All speedometers and gasoline pumps would likewise have a dual scale during this period.

On a more far-reaching level the Department of Transportation could require that a new model automobile be certified before it could be sold or operated on public highways. It could install standard traffic control techniques and enforce the regulations.

On a still more penetrating level, the Department of Transportation

[7] Most of these are needlessly wasted lives since there are much safer means of travel. There are 0.10 deaths per 10^9 passenger miles on trains, 0.27 on planes, and 2.2 in automobiles. If you must go from here to there you are ten times safer in a scheduled airliner than in your automobile.

could study the whole impact of mass transportation systems on our society. This would be generalized human factors engineering or a part of ecological engineering.

9.5   ECOLOGICAL ENGINEERING

The ecological engineer would call on the disciplines of human factors studies such as psychology, anthropology, and sociology as well as on the traditional physical and life sciences and classical engineering studies to aid in adapting technology to the needs of society. The ecological engineer is functioning today, although he may not realize it. There are presently under design complete colonies for living on the moon. These colonies will be in operation within 20 years or about the time you reach the prime of your professional life. No detail may be forgotten in such a colony. It will be a completely closed ecological system surrounded by a vacuum. Only occasional supply rockets will enter the system, and even here the input will be under complete control. We do not wish to pursue this general topic any further but will leave it for you to develop at your leisure. The preliminary design of a moon colony would make an excellent term design project.

We will limit ourselves to just one sample question in the way of an example of ecological engineering. Does the existence of a modern high-speed transportation system have any effect at all on the way a city should be laid out? The answer is Yes. Obviously the ideal shape for a city is 50 miles long and 4 blocks wide!

Since one rarely sees a city of this shape, perhaps we should explain our answer.[8] This solution represents a warping of the axes so that in effect the city is square. Along the central "spinal cord" a surface, mass-transportation system operates at 250 mi/hr. Thus to get from one end of the city to the other takes 15 to 20 minutes. This is the same length of time required to walk two blocks out to the green playing fields surrounding the city. This strip city could be bent to conform to natural formations such as a lake, river, or mountain. It could also be built in a circle with a circumference of 75 to 100 miles, with the 50-square-mile central area devoted to agriculture and recreation.

[8] We seem to have been anticipated here by science fiction. See, for example, T. Sturgeon, "How to Forget Baseball," *Sports Illustrated*, 21, No. 25, December 21, 1964, pp. 84 ff.

9.6   COMMUNICATION THEORY AND HUMAN FACTORS ENGINEERING

Communication theory and human factors engineering are intriguing subjects that have received considerable speculation but for which few results have been obtained as yet. We will discuss several areas in which the two fields of communication theory and human factors seem to contribute to one another, but we must look to the future for any major developments. Here are two examples of the use of the concept of channel capacity and information rate that are quite unlike those originally discussed by Shannon.

Channel Capacity of Living Organisms

J. G. Miller has studied the channel capacity of living organisms of various levels of complexity.[9] He finds that the general shape of performance curves is as shown in Fig. 9.1. Experimental evidence indicates

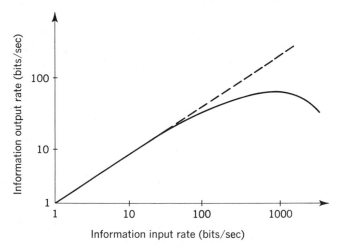

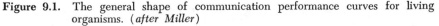

Figure 9.1.   The general shape of communication performance curves for living organisms. (*after Miller*)

[9] J. G. Miller, "Psychological Aspects of Communication Overloads," in *International Psychiatry Clinics,* Vol. 1 (Boston, Mass.: Little, Brown and Co.), January 1964, pp. 201–224.

that far below the peak capacity of the organism to react to and transmit information a linear relation holds. This simply indicates that, on the average, few mistakes are made for low transmission rates. Gradually, as the information input rate rises, mistakes begin to occur, and less information is properly transmitted. Finally, even if the information input continues to rise, the output rate fails to rise and then begins to fall.

Let us consider, for example, the optic nerve of the rat. If pulses of light followed by dark are impressed on the eye of the rat and the resultant potentials on the optic cortex of its brain are observed, the linear region of its performance curve is found to extend up to 10 bits/s. The peak transmission of 55 bits/s output occurs at 175 bits/s input information rate. The output rate then falls sharply even though the input rate is further increased. The gross peak rate occurs only at the expense of a significant number of errors, over 66 percent error in fact. If the organism were charged with these errors in some predetermined way, the peak net communication rate would be moved down closer to the limit of the linear region. This should be done if these data are to be used in design; however, the general shape of the curve would not change.

The rat's reaction to the light and transmission of a pulse to the optic cortex of its brain involves a rather complex organ. A similar pulse test applied to a single element of the sciatic nerve fiber of a frog and sensed at the axon of the same fiber involves only one neuron. (The neuron is the simplest building block of signal transmission in living organisms.) This test reveals a peak output rate of 4000 bits/s. at 20,000 bits/s input rate. The curve is of the same general shape shown in Figure 9.1 even though its peak occurs at a higher rate. For the more complex organ, the channel capacity is twenty times less than that of the single neuron.

By this reasoning, still more complex organisms, such as a human being, made up of many separate sensing and transmission organs, should exhibit an even slower rate of response than the rat. And indeed this is so. Miller's human subjects were presented with a light flashing at various intervals and were expected to respond by pressing a lever as soon as possible after seeing the light flash. The evidence shows a peak output rate of about 5.75 bits/s for an input rate of 10 bits/s.

Miller continued his experiments by testing more complex groups. He defines a group as consisting of three persons arranged in a task, as shown in Figure 9.2. An input pulse causes a light to go on simultaneously before two subjects. As rapidly as possible the subjects are to

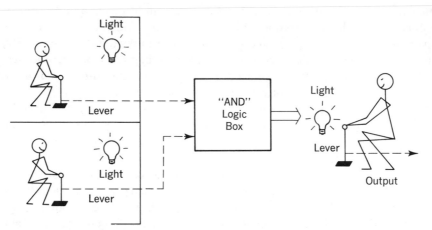

Figure 9.2.   A two-level group in a communication rate experiment.

move their levers in response to their light. Only when both levers are moved is the pulse transmitted to the second level. At the second level, a subject responds by moving his lever as his light flashes. It is not difficult to guess that the group will have a lower peak transmission rate than will the individual. The test shows the peak output rate is about 3.75 bits/s for an input rate of 5.5 bits/s.

Further work with organizations of three separate echelons was also carried out. The organization's input echelon consisted of two groups of two subjects each, as shown in Figure 9.3. One group of two subjects formed the second or decider echelon, and a single subject was the output echelon. The echelons were physically separate. Each subject in the first group of the input echelon responded to the first of two flashes by pushing a lever. Each subject in the second group responded similarly to the second flash. These sections flashed lights before the decider echelon, which responded to the flashes made by the first echelon, each subject pressing his lever in response to the two flashes activated by the groups in the first echelon. Subjects in this second echelon did not respond until after seeing two flashes from the input echelon, thus correcting for erroneous extra pushes of a member of the input groups but not for omissions. The single subject in the third echelon responded to the output of the second echelon, pressing his lever for all flashes. His signals were the organization's output. The channel capacity of this organization was about 2.5 bits/s at an input rate of about 4.0 bits/s.

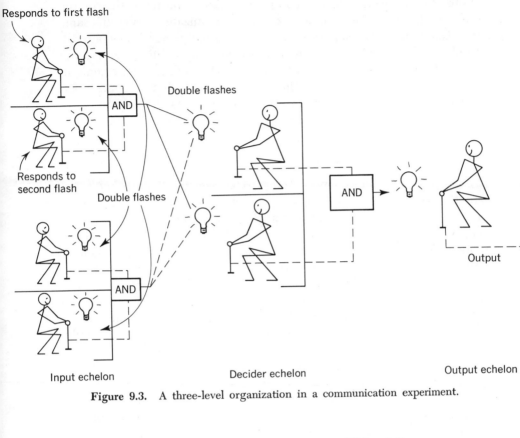

Figure 9.3. A three-level organization in a communication experiment.

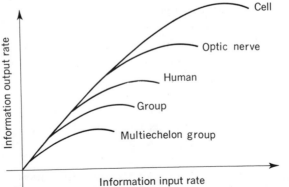

Figure 9.4. Theoretical curves based on performance data on five levels of living systems. (*after Miller*)

Note that the peak rate for a human is about one tenth that of the simpler optic organ. Tests on more complex organizations show the same trend continuing. A complex social organization would show a peak rate of less than 1 bit/s. Perhaps this indicates the limiting size for the hierarchical form of social organization. As it grows in size, its communication rate decreases, and thus the speed with which the organization can mobilize itself to react to reward or to punishment decreases. Figure 9.4 shows the performance curves for five levels of living systems.

Auto Traffic and Channel Capacity

A number of workers have attempted to construct a mathematical model of the flow of traffic on a highway. As the level of traffic rises all over the United States and highways become more and more expensive, it seems apparent that engineering design principles must be made to include an estimate of the peak capacity of a proposed section of highway and an estimate of how various factors affect this peak capacity. It is possible to consider each vehicle as a "bit" of information and the highway as a communication channel. Thus, the concept of channel capacity has direct relevance here. We will note, for example, the similarity in shape of the curves just discussed with those derived for traffic flow.

It is not sufficient simply to use data gathered on the open highway to estimate the traffic flow through critical points. Critical points or bottlenecks are special situations such as tunnels, bridges, intersections, and sharp curves. It is very difficult to formulate general principles for predicting the flow through bottlenecks because the flow is critically dependent on the psychological reaction of individual drivers to real or imagined stimuli. For example, suppose you are on an interstate highway with no grade crossings and wide spacing between the flow of traffic in each direction. You are approaching a tunnel cut through a ridge of rock. The tunnel is short and brightly lighted, and you can see daylight at the other end. The road remains flat, and the road lanes do not narrow. Yet the normal tendency is to slow down as you approach the tunnel and to speed up again as you leave it. This is a psychological bottleneck and is perhaps just as real as a physical narrowing of the road.

Present traffic studies concentrate on special situations. For example, for simplicity a "no passing" or "no changing lanes" requirement is often imposed on theoretical studies. This is a realistic requirement in bottlenecks, and therefore the restriction should not invalidate the theory

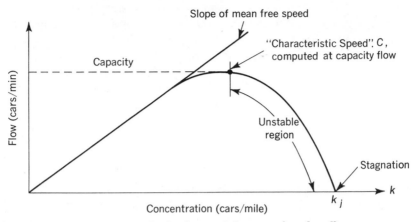

Figure 9.5.   The fundamental diagram of road traffic.

in such situations. Suppose we consider a single lane of traffic and relate concentration of traffic to the average flow.[10] Such a relation is shown in Figure 9.5.

Let us consider the meaning of this relation. Suppose the traffic is very light on a certain portion of road in which we are interested. Each driver feels alone, so he adjusts his speed to suit himself. These freely selected speeds cluster about a mean free speed in approximately a Gaussian distribution as shown in Figure 9.6. For low traffic concentrations, the flow increases linearly with concentration. Gradually as the concentration continues to increase, the drivers begin to react to one another, and the flow fails to increase linearly. Finally a peak flow is reached, and increased concentration beyond this value results in traffic slow down, a traffic jam, and finally stagnation, that is, a complete stoppage. Greenberg,[11] has proposed an equation that matches experimental flow-concentration data quite well.

$$q = ck \ln (k_j/k) \tag{9.1}$$

where $q \triangleq$ flow, (cars/hr)
  $k \triangleq$ concentration (cars/mi)
  $k_j \triangleq$ jam concentration (cars/mi)
  $c \triangleq$ optimum speed (maximum flow speed) (mi/hr)

---

[10] F. A. Haight, *Mathematical Theories of Traffic Flow* (New York: Academic Press, Inc., 1963), p. 72.
[11] H. Greenberg, "An Analysis of Traffic Flow," *Operation Research.* **7**, 1959, pp. 79–85.

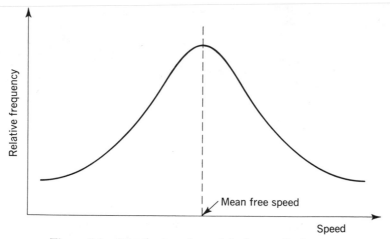

Figure 9.6.   Distribution of speed for low traffic density.

where ln is the natural logarithm and c and k_j are constants for a particular road segment.

Greenberg postulated the classical equation of motion for a one-dimensional fluid in addition to the continuity equation, and he deduced Equation (9.1). Data from experiments on the Lincoln Tunnel, for example yield $c = 20$ mi/hr and $k_j = 220$ cars/mi.[12] The parameters c and k_j depend upon the particular stretch of road under test. Since Greenberg's equation accurately predicts single-lane traffic,[13] it has design value. The Holland Tunnel is older than the Lincoln Tunnel and its "characteristic speed" is smaller, $c = 18$ mi/hr whereas the Queens-Midtown Tunnel has a characteristic speed of $c = 22$ mi/hr.[14] Note that the region between peak capacity and stagnation in Figure 9.5 is unstable. That is, it is impossible to maintain steady-state operation at any point on this portion of the curve. Suppose there exists at some instant a concentration and flow that places the operation on this portion of the curve. Now, if for some reason the concentration were momentarily to increase,

[12] R. Herman and R. B. Potts, "Single-Lane Traffic Theory and Experiment," in R. Herman, ed., *Theory of Traffic Flow* (Princeton, N.J.: D. Van Nostrand Co., Inc., 1961), pp. 120–146.

[13] L. C. Edie and R. S. Foote, "Experiments on Single-Lane Flow in Tunnels," in R. Herman, ed., *Theory of Traffic Flow*, pp. 175–192 (see footnote 12).

[14] R. Herman and K. Gardels, "Vehicular Traffic Flow," *Scientific American,* **209,** No. 6, December 1963, pp. 35–43.

this would decrease the flow and the speed (arguing simply from physical considerations). If the flow drops, we see from the curve that this further increases the concentration. Thus we argue that the operating point, once it passes the peak capacity, slides down the curve until a traffic jam occurs. Robert Herman reports, for example, that no one has ever observed a steadily moving stream of traffic with a concentration of more than about 110 vehicles per mile in a lane.

EXAMPLE 9.1

Find the mean free speed in the Lincoln Tunnel by the use of Equation (9.1). Discuss the accuracy of fit in the low flow-concentration range. The characteristic speed in the Lincoln Tunnel has been found to be $c =$ mi/hr, and the jam concentration is $k_j = 220$ cars/mi. A plot of Equation (9.1) for these coefficients is shown in Figure 9.7. For

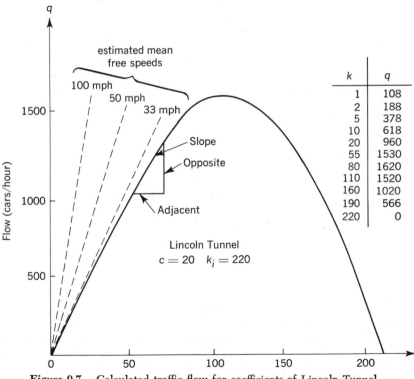

k	q
1	108
2	188
5	378
10	618
20	960
55	1530
80	1620
110	1520
160	1020
190	566
220	0

Figure 9.7. Calculated traffic flow for coefficients of Lincoln Tunnel.

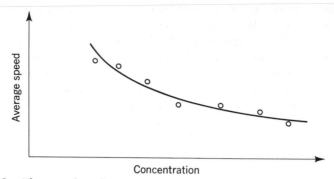

Figure 9.8. Theoretical and experimental speed-concentration data for Lincoln Tunnel. (Edie, Foote, p. 185, figure 10)

low concentration no portion of the curve is a straight line; therefore it is a matter of judgment where a straight line approximation should be drawn. For the scale of this plot, a fit to the lower portion of the curve yields a mean free speed of 100 mi/hr. This is too high, of course. A 50 mi/hr curve shows a reasonable fit. Tests reported by Herman and Potts[15] seem to indicate that a figure of 30 to 35 mi/hr for low flow is closer to actuality. Thus Equation (9.1) fails to represent reality in the region from 0 to 10 cars/mi. This range is not important, and the excellent fit with experimental data for the range from 10 cars/mi up through the full capacity flow is sufficient justification for its use. Figure 9.8 shows a comparison of the theory based on Greenberg's equation and experimental data.

The slope, or *derivative*, of the curve in Figure 9.7 has the following units.

$$\text{Slope} = \frac{\text{opposite}}{\text{adjacent}} = \frac{\text{cars/hr}}{\text{cars/mi}} = \frac{\text{mi}}{\text{hr}}$$

Thus the slope of the curve is the average speed at that concentration. This derivative is plotted versus concentration in Figure 9.8, along with experimental data. The fit in the region of interest is excellent.

We might argue that this analysis is all very well but really not very important. This reasoning has not told us how to construct a road that will have a higher capacity for lower cost, for example, and it seems

[15] Herman and Potts, p. 141 (see footnote 12).

only common sense to say that there is some optimum concentration for which the flow is maximum. The analytic approach is interesting, but the essence of the engineering method is its predictive value. Therefore we ask, "What predictive or design value does the theory based on Equation (9.1) have?"

We close this discussion of traffic flow with an example of such a design use. Greenberg has proposed a control scheme based on the foregoing analysis. When carried out experimentally by Edie and Foote, a significant increase in the rush hour traffic has been obtained.[16] This is certainly an example of the predictive power of this work because the approach involves periodically interrupting traffic. The traffic is halted in order to increase the net flow, which seems contrary to intuition.

Greenberg noted that during rush-hour periods in the New York Port Authority tunnels, the concentration exceeded the optimum value established by the single-lane traffic-flow relation [see Equation (9.1)]. The average speed of the traffic decreased and the net flow went down. Greenberg studied the behavior of drivers in rush-hour traffic in some detail. He noted that the exact mechanism by which flow is reduced is as follows. In most under-river tunnels there is a downgrade for cars entering the tunnel; then near the end there is a distinct upgrade to the exit. The grade may be as much as 3.5 percent. The beginning of the upgrade constitutes a bottleneck because the average driver is somewhat disoriented by his surroundings and fails to adjust the pressure on the accelerator to maintain his speed as he begins the upgrade. This lag in speed transmits itself backward along the column of traffic and is accentuated by drivers whose reactions are too strong and who tend to tail gate (such as college freshmen). Good drivers whose sensitivity is lower and who space themselves more conservatively (such as the average college professor) add a stabilizing influence. Greenberg suggested that this accordion, wavelike motion could be limited by deliberately introducing gaps in the line of traffic. Edie and Foote tested this idea by counting forty-four cars and then halting traffic until a total of 2 minutes had elapsed from the time the first car entered the tunnel. They found these platoons of automobiles (forty-four every 2 minutes) proceeded through the tunnel more expeditiously than could a constant stream of traffic. Although some wave motion was noted, it was confined to one platoon. The results of this test are given in Table 9.1.

[16] Edie and Foote, see footnote 13. Herman and Gardels, see footnote 14.

**Table 9.1   Results of Platooning Forty-four Automobiles every
2 Minutes through Single Lane of Holland Tunnel***

PERFORMANCE QUANTITY	CHANGE (IN PERCENT)
Traffic flow	6–10 increase
Traffic velocity	29 increase
Breakdowns from stop-and-go traffic	63 decrease
Carbon-monoxide level in tunnel	11 decrease
Electricity used in tunnel ventilation	10 decrease

* From Edie and Foote (see footnote 13).

These results have been so successful that special automatic traffic centers and control lights are being installed in the Port Authority tunnels in New York City. The net effect will be as though an additional lane were added at no cost. This is certainly an engineering accomplishment of which to be proud.

CHAPTER TEN

Optimization Theory

10.1 INTRODUCTION

We have seen that design is an iterative process. One begins with an ill-formulated problem and gradually defines it in a meaningful way and finds an acceptable solution by repetitively applying the steps of recognition, comparison, evaluation, and iteration.

Generally a point is reached in this iterative process at which the problem is sufficiently well formulated so that the remainder of the design process can be expressed in terms of a step-by-step procedure for solution or *algorithm*. For example, in problems to which Kelvin's law may be applied, we seek to minimize the total cost. Occasionally the cost function can be expressed analytically in terms of one or more adjustable parameters. Then by straightforward differentiation, we can find the location of the point of zero slope on the cost curve and thus the optimum settings for the design parameters. Those problems in which an *index of performance*[1] (IP) such as zero slope is defined and the available parameters are adjusted so as to optimize this index of performance are called *optimization problems.* In such problems the available parameters can be adjusted either analytically or experimentally.

Notice that we may wish to minimize or maximize the IP, depending on the problem. While total cost is to be minimized, traffic flow in a tunnel is to be maximized. The two cases are similar in that we seek the zero slope point on the performance function in each, and, in fact, the mathematical methods used to find these points are identical.

Properly interpreted we could say that *all* engineering design problems are optimization problems. Experienced engineers might argue with this statement by saying, "No, at my shop we don't give a darn about the best possible solution; we don't have the time for that. We just want to find any solution that will work and do it as quickly as possible." In a broad sense, however, this engineer *is* optimizing. But his index of performance includes a heavy weighting for the cost of design time.

In this chapter we will discuss several of the simpler analytic methods that are useful in optimization problems.

10.2   OPTIMIZATION OF A SINGLE PARAMETER: CALCULUS

Suppose you are given a function of a single variable

$$y = f(x) \tag{10.1}$$

and are asked to find the value of x for which y is a maximum. Provided we can differentiate $f(x)$ and no restrictions are placed on the allowable values of x, this is not a difficult problem. Common sense tells us that the top of the hill occurs at the value of x for which the slope is zero. This is diagramed in Figure 10.1. Thus we need only solve for this value of x. Suppose, for example,

$$y = f(x) = -x^2 + 4x + 3 \tag{10.2}$$

[1] Also called *objective function, cost function,* and *value function.*

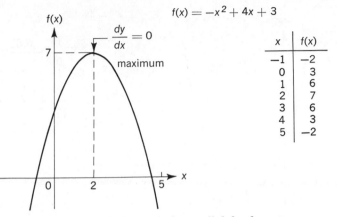

$$f(x) = -x^2 + 4x + 3$$

x	f(x)
−1	−2
0	3
1	6
2	7
3	6
4	3
5	−2

Figure 10.1.   A function with a well-defined maximum.

Then the slope is

$$\frac{dy}{dx} = -2x + 4$$

Now equate the slope to zero, and solve for x

$$-2x + 4 = 0$$
$$x = 2$$

In order to find the maximum value of the function substitute back into $f(x)$ to find its value at $x = 2$:

$$f(2) = -(2)^2 + 4(2) + 3 = 7$$

The mathematician would call zero slope a *necessary condition* for a maximum, but it is not sufficient. Suppose, for example, we consider the following function

$$y = f(x) = x^2 - 4x + 3 \qquad (10.3)$$

Now

$$\frac{dy}{dx} = 2x - 4$$

and setting this equal to zero still yields $x = 2$ as the point of zero slope. But it is obvious if $f(x)$ is plotted, as in Figure 10.2, that $x = 2$ is now the location of a minimum, not a maximum. We might say, then,

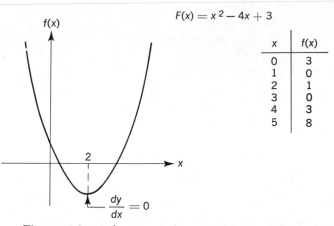

$$F(x) = x^2 - 4x + 3$$

x	f(x)
0	3
1	0
2	1
3	0
4	3
5	8

Figure 10.2.   A function with a well-defined minimum.

that a zero slope location is a candidate for a maximum, that is, a point worthy of further consideration.

EXAMPLE 10.1   KELVIN'S LAW

In Chapter 5 one of the assignments concerned the calculation of the optimum height of an office building. Let us return now to that problem and solve it by differentiation. Total cost equals cost of materials plus cost of labor and services, or

$$C_t = C_1 + C_2$$

We are given

$$C_1 = \frac{100,000}{f/2} \text{ (dollars)}$$

and

$$C_2 = 1000f \text{ (dollars)}$$

where f is the number of floors. Thus

$$C_t = \frac{100,000}{f/2} + 1000f$$

Differentiate the cost function and set the result equal to zero

$$\frac{dC_t}{df} = \frac{-200,000}{f^2} + 1000 = 0$$

Thus

$$f^2 = 200$$

and

$$f = 14.15 \approx 14 \text{ floors}$$

10.3 SEARCH USING LOCAL SLOPE: THE GRADIENT METHOD

An engineer is often faced with an optimization problem on a physical system for which he does not have an analytic expression such as Equations (10.1), (10.2), or (10.3), which may be differentiated. Often he will find it possible to record only the setting of a parameter and the performance of the device for that given parameter setting. Such a situation is diagramed in Figure 10.3. Because the sketch is simple, do not be deceived into thinking that this is a trivial problem. The black box could be an oil refinery, chemical process, steel mill, or electric utility. The principle is the same. The object is to adjust the lever x so that the process $f(x)$ achieves a maximum or minimum. Instead of asking

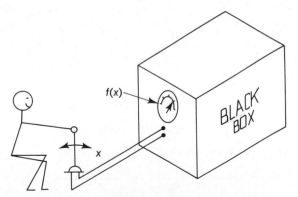

Figure 10.3. A black box optimization problem.

a man to find the optimum setting, it is possible to build a control device that will do it automatically. Two logical ways in which either the man or the automatic control device could accomplish the task are

1.   *Discrete gradient:* small step-by-step adjustments which permit a decision to move the $f(x)$ pointer in the correct direction.

2.   *Continuous gradient:* small continuous oscillatory motions of the x handle which cause a resulting smooth motion in $f(x)$. Comparison of the cause and effect will permit a decision to be made as to the desirable direction in which to move x.

The discrete gradient method would be carried out using a digital computer and associated logic elements. To be specific, let us propose a logic scheme that will insure reaching the maximum of a hill with a single well-defined peak such as that shown in Figure 10.4 using this method.

1.   Record a pair of values x_1 and $f(x_1)$.
2.   Increase x_1 by Δx and record x_2 and $f(x_2)$.
3.   For $\Delta x > 0$ and $\Delta f(x) > 0$; Δx should be positive.
     For $\Delta x > 0$ and $\Delta f(x) < 0$; Δx should be negative.
     For $\Delta x < 0$ and $\Delta f(x) > 0$; Δx should be negative.
     For $\Delta x < 0$ and $\Delta f(x) < 0$; Δx should be positive.
4.   Choose correct sign for Δx and continue until $\Delta f(x) = 0$.

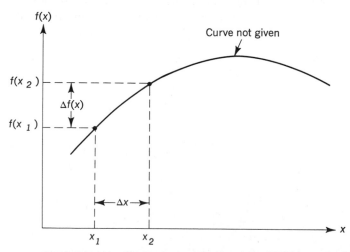

Figure 10.4.   The discrete gradient scheme; the curve is drawn in only for clarity. It is not given a priori.

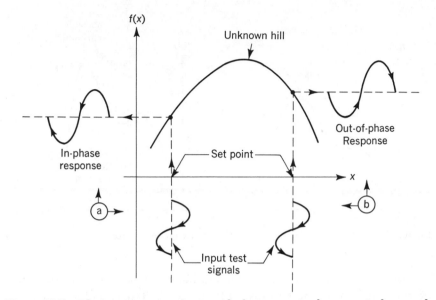

Figure 10.5. The continuous gradient method, once again the curve is drawn only for clarity. Two situations are (a) input in phase with output and (b) input and output out of phase.

An equally valuable procedure but one that is carried out with an analog computer and associated equipment is the continuous gradient technique diagramed in Figure 10.5. Here a small sinusoidal perturbation or test signal is introduced into x. There will occur a resultant perturbation in $f(x)$. The logic scheme is as follows.

1. If the perturbation in x and $f(x)$ are *in phase*—that is, when x goes up, $f(x)$ goes up and when x goes down, $f(x)$ goes down— the setting for x is less than the peak value, and the setting should be increased [shown at (a) on Figure 10.5].

2. If the perturbation in x is *out of phase* with $f(x)$—that is, when x goes up, $f(x)$ goes down—the setting for x is above the optimum value and should be decreased [shown at (b) on Figure 10.5].

A computer program to automate the discrete gradient search would be even more complex than the scheme given above. For example, how does one choose the magnitude of Δx? If Δx is too large, the optimum value will be missed completely, and the system will continue to *hunt* back and forth around the optimum value but never find it.

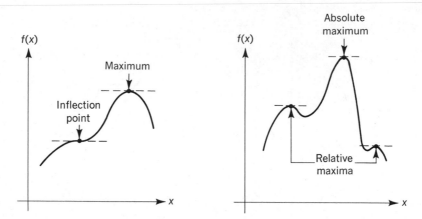

Figure 10.6. Nonunimodal hills; such functions are unsuitable for gradient search.

Moreover, although in theory the gradient method will work for curves of the type shown in Figures 10.1 and 10.2, it may fail for functions such as those shown in Figure 10.6. Gradient methods of hill climbing are acceptable provided the hill is unimodal. A *unimodal* function (hill) is one with one and only one maximum (or minimum as the case may be) and no inflection points or discontinuities. The hills in Figure 10.1 and 10.2 are unimodal, but the hills in Figure 10.6 are not.

Even when the hill is unimodal, there are sometimes excellent reasons for not choosing a gradient search method. Such a situation arises if the measuring technique is costly and it is desired to find the extremum[2] with the minimum number of measurements.

10.4   FIBONACCI SEARCH AND THE GOLDEN MEAN

Suppose we seek the extremum of a hill known to be unimodal. It is known that an extremum exists within a range of values 0 to x_0. Suppose each measurement costs time and money, and therefore we wish to discover the extremum with the least number of measurements. Is there some scheme for distributing the location of discrete measurements in such a way that we are sure that no other scheme of placement can

---

[2] An extremum is an extreme value and can be either a maximum or a minimum.

be devised using fewer measurements? J. Kiefer[3] has shown that the answer to this question is Yes. Kiefer's method involves the use of the Fibonacci series,

$$F_0 = F_1 = 1 : F_n = F_{n-1} + F_{n-2}$$

or

$$F = 1, 1, 2, 3, 5, 8, 13, \cdots$$

This series occurs in a number of seemingly unrelated areas.

As shown in Figure 10.7, we divide the search interval into two lengths by choosing the first measurement point. The length of one of the segments R to the total length L is in the ratio

$$\frac{R}{L} = \frac{F_{n-1}}{F_n} + \frac{(-1)^n \epsilon}{F_n}$$

where n is the number of measurements we have decided a priori to take and ϵ is a small number ($\epsilon \ll 1$). We can see by examining the Fibonacci series that for n large ($n > 8$), the ratio of two adjacent Fibonacci numbers approaches a constant

$$\frac{R}{L} \approx \frac{F_{n-1}}{F_n} \approx 0.618 \qquad (n > 8)$$

This ratio is not without interest itself. Euclid calls it the golden section or the *golden mean*. He defines a length divided into two unequal segments such that the ratio of the length of the whole to the larger

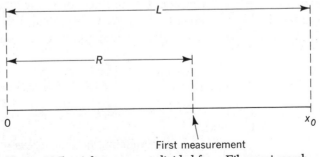

Figure 10.7.   A line segment divided for a Fibonacci search.

[3] J. Kiefer, "Sequential Minimax Search for a Maximum," *Proc. Am. Math Soc.,* **4,** 1953, p. 502.

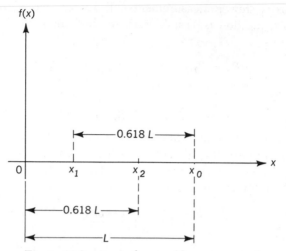

Figure 10.8.   Logic for a golden mean search.

segment is equal to the ratio of the length of the larger to the smaller as the golden section. The Greeks endowed this ratio with mystic properties and felt it to be the most pleasing ratio of width to length of any rectangle. The golden mean was used throughout Greek construction and survives today in architecture and graphic design.

For $n < 8$ the ratio of two Fibonacci numbers is not constant, and this immensely complicates a digital computer program designed to conduct a Fibonacci search. The thought occurs, then, to question if a constant golden mean ratio search would be significantly inferior to a precise Fibonacci search. It is not. In fact, at worst, the golden mean search could only be 17 percent worse than the ideal Fibonacci. (If we are lucky, on a particular hill it could be just as good or even better.)

Now let us develop the logic of a golden mean search to find the maximum of a single-dimensional unimodal hill. (See Figure 10.8.)

1. The first two readings are taken at x_1 and x_2, located at $0.618L$ from either end.

    a.   If $f(x_1) > f(x_2)$, the maximum lies between 0 and x_2. Thus choose this as the next interval.

    b.   If $f(x_1) < f(x_2)$, the maximum lies between x_1 and L, thus choose this as the next interval.

    c.   If $f(x_1) = f(x_2)$, choose either of the above intervals.

2.   With the new reduced interval, repeat step 1. Note that only one new measurement is needed, since one of the preceding measurements lies at precisely the correct location for this present determination.

3.   Continue until the maximum is located to within as small an interval as desired. Note that we need not specify a priori the number of steps. Thus the computer program consists of a single loop and "if" statements specifying the desired interval.

EXAMPLE 10.2

Find the maximum of

$$f(x) = -x^2 + 4x + 3 \qquad (10.4)$$

In the interval, $0 \le x \le 10$ by golden mean search. A maximum ambiguity of 1 percent of the original interval will be permitted.[4] The original length is 10 units. Thus $x_1 = 3.82$, and $x_2 = 6.18$, and we have

$$f(x_1) = f(3.82) = 3.68$$

and

$$f(x_2) = f(6.18) = 10.5$$

Since $f(x_1) > f(x_2)$, the maximum lies between $0 \le x \le x_2$. The new length is 6.18 units, and the golden mean points on this new interval are $x_3 = 2.36$ and $x_1 = 3.82$. Only one of these values requires a new calculation

$$f(x_3) = f(2.36) = 5.56$$
$$f(x_1) = f(3.82) = 3.68$$

Thus the maximum lies between $0 \le x \le 3.8$. Continue this procedure until the maximum is located to within as small an interval of x as desired.

10.5   SEARCH FOR EXTREMA OF NON-UNIMODAL HILLS

There are a variety of ad hoc techniques available for search of non-unimodal hills, but no such neat analytic method as a Fibonacci search

[4] Of course this is merely an academic problem, since by simple differentiation of Equation (10.4) we could find the maximum to be located at precisely $x = 2$. In practice, the golden mean or Fibonacci search would be used when the explicit function relationship is not given.

exists. Really the problem is beyond the level of this text, but we mention it to let you know we are interested in it.

10.6   CALCULUS OF VARIATIONS AND EXTREMIZATION OF FUNCTIONALS

This is also beyond the level of this text, but your mathematical friends will be very impressed if you say that you have studied a text where the subject was mentioned.

The problem develops in the following way. Many optimization problems can be formulated by choosing an entire function rather than simply one value of a function. This occurs in choosing an optimum path from here to there according to some extremizing rule or law. This is an extremely messy business and is the subject of a great deal of exciting research at the graduate level. For example, it would be nice to know the optimum path from the earth to the moon and back so that we could move a maximum payload with a minimum fuel expenditure.

For certain simple problems of this sort, the classical calculus of variations will suffice. There are not very many such problems, however, which may be why books on the subject contain so few examples and exercises. Newer developments such as Dynamic Programming and the Maximum Principle of Pontriagin hold considerable promise in this area.

PROBLEMS

10.1   Derive the value of the golden mean.

10.2   By differentiation of Equation (9.1), find the optimum concentration k and maximum flow q at that concentration for the Lincoln Tunnel.

10.3   Assume a parabolic hill such as is shown in Figure 10.5. Pick x_0 at the optimum value, and show the effect on $f(x)$ of linearly varying x about its optimum x_0. Plot $f(x)$ versus time. Show the hunting loss, defined as the difference between the average $f(x)$ and the optimum $f(x)$.

Booklist for Engineers[1]

Biographies of Engineers and Engineering Scientists

An attempt has been made to find materials that portray the interesting lives that such men have lived as well as the important work they have accomplished. These books show how the motivation of the engineer differs from that of the scientist; the engineer's desire is to solve the problems that must be solved rather than merely to learn the facts of nature.

Early Scientists and Inventors

Armitage, Angus. *Sun, Stand Thou Still; the Life and Work of Copernicus, the Astronomer.* New York: Henry Schuman, Inc., Publishers, 1947.

> The life of the man who overthrew the belief that the earth was fixed at the center of the universe.

Bell, Eric Temple. *Men of Mathematics.* New York: Simon and Schuster, Inc., 1937.

> Stories of the lives and achievements of the great mathematicians from Zeno to Poincare and Cantor.

[1] Extracted from a list prepared by the Purdue chapter of Tau Beta Pi, the engineering honor society.

Harsanyi, Zsolt. *The Star-gazer*. New York: G. P. Putnam's Sons, 1939.
A powerful historical novel retelling the story of Galileo.

Hart, Ivor B. *Makers of Science*. London: Oxford University Press, 1924.
A connected story of some of the broader movements in the field of the physical and mathematical sciences.

Merezhkovskii, Dimitrii S. *The Romance of Leonardo da Vinci*. New York: Random House, Inc., 1928.
A full-length portrait of one of the world's most remarkable geniuses and the times in which he lived.

More, Louis T. *Isaac Newton*. New York: Charles Scribner's Sons, 1934.
A detailed biography of the "greatest of scientific geniuses" based on extensive research.

Struik, Dirk Jan. *A Concise History of Mathematics*. New York: Dover Publications, Inc., 1948.
Two thoughtful volumes relating mathematics to the history of culture.

Mechanical Engineers

Carnegie, Andrew. *James Watt*. New York: Doubleday, Page, and Company, 1905.
Carnegie has woven into his biography of the inventor of the steam engine his own philosophy of success, drawing upon his personal experience to point the morals found in his hero's life.

Dickinson, Henry Winram. *Matthew Boulton*. London: Cambridge University Press, 1937.
A book about Boulton's many-sided genius as metal worker, partner to Watt, and improver of coinage with special stress on the man's technical achievements.

Dickinson, Henry Winram and Arthur Titley. *Richard Trevithick, the Engineer and the Man*. London: Cambridge University Press, 1934.
The personality and career of an English engineer who was the principal worker in the early development of the high-pressure steam engine.

Larsen, Egon. *An American in Europe*. New York: Philosophical Library 1953.
An entertaining biography of Benjamin Thompson, Count Rumford, a Massachusetts farmer's son who gained fame in England, Bavaria and France. Among his many activities, he was a pioneer in domestic

science, the creator of the modern theory of heat, the first nutrition expert, and the discoverer of Humphrey Davy.

Leupp, Francis E. *George Westinghouse; His Life and Achievements.* Boston: Little, Brown, and Co., 1918.

A comprehensive survey in narrative form of Westinghouse's achievements in the mechanical and electrical arts, together with an intimate picture of the man and his family life.

Mirsky, Jeanette and Allan Nevins. *The World of Eli Whitney.* New York: The Macmillan Company, 1952.

Whitney was not just a clever mechanic. He was a man of ideas; his real life is the life of his mind. This book tries to explain it.

Nevins, Allan. *Ford: The Times, the Man, the Company.* New York: Charles Scribner's Sons, 1954.

A comprehensive, extensively documented study of Henry Ford, the car he built, and the company he formed, set against the background of American economic life and ideals.

Chemical and Metallurgical Engineers

Cameron, Frank Thomas. *Cottrell, Samaritan of Science.* Garden City, N.Y.: Doubleday & Company, Inc., 1952.

This excellent biography gives an insight into Frederick G. Cottrell's almost endless contributions to applied science, his boundless curiosity and enthusiasm for all things scientific, and his ability to solve seemingly unsolvable problems.

Conant, James B., editor. *Robert Boyle's Experiments in Pneumatics.* Cambridge, Mass.: Harvard University Press, 1950.

A case history of pneumatic experiments, 1630–1680, providing a basis for new ideas and also a change of attitude toward science.

Fermi, Laura. *Atoms in the Family; My Life with Enrico Fermi.* Chicago: University of Chicago Press, 1954.

An entertaining informal and informative biography of one of the foremost theoretical physicists of our day, written by his wife.

Hammond, John Hays. *The Autobiography of John Hays Hammond.* New York: Farrar and Rinehart, vol. 2, 1935.

An interesting adventure story, full of information about mining history and the development of the backward regions of the earth.

Holt, Anne. *Life of Joseph Priestly.* London: Oxford University Press, 1931.

Priestly, as chemist, theologian, discoverer of oxygen, and inventor of soda water, has many claims to remembrance.

Hoover, Herbert Clark. *Memoire*. New York: The Macmillan Company, 1951. Vol. 1, *Years of Adventure, 1874–1920*.

The first volume of ex-President Hoover's memoirs sketches his life from his birth, through his engineering career, to 1920, when he became Secretary of Commerce in the Harding cabinet.

McKie, Douglas. *Antoine Lavoisier: Scientist, Economist, Social Reformer*. New York: H. Schuman, 1952.

The "father of modern chemistry" was also a social reformer who was one of the victims of the French Revolution.

Wheeler, Lynde Phelps. *Josiah Willard Gibbs, the History of a Great Mind*. New Haven: Yale University Press, 1951.

The story of a great U.S. scientist, whose paper on the Equilibrium of Heterogeneous Substances is the basis of much present day chemical and engineering theory.

Civil Engineers

Bishop, Joseph B. *Goethals, Genius of the Panama Canal*. New York: Harper, 1930.

A personal view of the man who completed the Canal in the face of difficulties of disease and morale even more serious than the engineering problems of the task.

Cooley, Mortimer E. *Scientific Blacksmith*. New York: American Society of Mechanical Engineers, 1947.

Unpretentious reminiscence by an engineer about his life and professional career. Valuable for its practical discussion of the problems an engineer faces.

Darrah, William C. *Powell of the Colorado*. Princeton, N.J.: Princeton University Press, 1951.

A thorough, documented study of the life of John Wesley Powell, first head of the U.S. Geological Survey, a pioneer in developing federal administration of reclamation and conservation, and an effective advocate of the role of science in government.

Hungerford, Edward. *Daniel Willard Rides the Line*. New York: G. P. Putnam's Sons, 1938.

A sympathetic portrait of the B & O president, who rose from the ranks and who knew his job and the people who worked for him.

Jewett, A. C. *An American Engineer in Afghanistan.* Minneapolis, Minn.: University of Minnesota Press, 1948.

> A story of engineering achievement in the face of great difficulties in an underdeveloped country.

Siegfried, Andra. *Suez and Panama.* New York: Harcourt, Brace, 1940.

> A skillfully written account of the two great canals and the man who created them, particularly de Lesseps, the famous French engineer.

Steinman, David B. *The Builders of the Bridge; the Story of John Roebling and his Son.* New York: Harcourt, Brace, 1945.

> A biographical study by an eminent present day bridge engineer of two men who were pioneers in bridge design and who combined imagination with technical skill.

Stevens, John F. "An Engineer's Recollections," Parts 1–13 in *Engineering News-Record,* Vol. 114 (Jan.–June 1935), pp. 412–414; 450–452; 521–524; 590–592; 672–675; 749–751; 850–852; 917–919; and Vol. 115 (July–Dec. 1935), pp. 216–217; 255–257; 330–333; 643–646; 740–742.

> The experience of an engineer who helped open the West to the railroad. He believes that young engineers still have before them wider fields for pioneer effort than were open to his own generation.

Electrical Engineers

Crowther, James G. *Men of Science: Humphrey Davy, Michael Faraday, James Prescott Joule, William Thomson, James Clark Maxwell.* New York: Norton, 1936.

> An attempt to relate scientists and the society in which they work. Although the reader may not agree with the author's point of view, it is a stimulating one.

De Forest, Lee. *Father of Radio; the Autobiography of Lee De Forest.* Chicago: Wilcox and Follett, 1950.

> A biography interesting for the light it sheds on the development of electronics and for its portrayal of an extraordinary personality.

Dunlap, Orrin E. *Radio's 100 Men of Science.* New York: Harper, 1944.

> Presents the evolution of a science in terms of the personalities of the men who created it.

Dyer, Frank L. *Edison, his Life and Inventions.* New York: Harper, 1910.

> A well written and full account of the life of the inventor.

Everson, George. *The Story of Television, Life of Philo T. Farnsworth.*
New York: Norton, 1949.
    A story of perseverance, originality, and a new science told from
    a personal and intimate knowledge of the man and his work.
Pupin, Michael. *From Immigrant to Inventor.* New York: Scribners, 1923.
    A clear account of the meaning of modern science coupled with
    the story of the Americanization of an immigrant.

Aeronautics

Lindbergh, Charles. *The Spirit of St. Louis.* New York: Scribner, 1953.
    America's most noted pilot uses his famous Atlantic crossing as
    the framework of his personal view of the growth of American
    aviation.
Morris, Lloyd R. *Ceiling Unlimited.* New York: Macmillan, 1953.
    Covers many of the early engineers: Langley, Chanute, Curtiss,
    and the Wright brothers, and discusses their contribution to the
    air age.
Norway, Nevil Shute. *Slide Rule, by Nevil Shute.* New York: Morrow,
1954.
    Noted mainly for his novels, the writer tells here of his work in
    aeronautics with emphasis on the problem of designing and testing
    the dirigible R-100.
Exupery, Antoine de Saint. *Wind, Sand and Stars.* New York: Reynal
& Hitchcock, 1940.
    In this classic of aeronautical literature the French flier-writer tells
    of the experiences air travel brought to him.
Wright, Wilbur. *The Papers of Wilbur and Orville Wright.* New York:
McGraw-Hill, 1953.
    Every grain of excitement that preceded the first powered flight
    has been successfully transferred to the pages of this detailed two
    volume history.

SECTION II
Histories of Science and Engineering

These books show how engineering and related scientific activities
have contributed to the progress of civilization—not only to the obvious
improvement of man's comfort, health and prosperity, but also to the

advancement of his aesthetic and moral ideas and perceptions and to the molding of political and social institutions.

Baker, Moses Nelson. *The Quest for Pure Water.* New York: American Water Works Assn., 1948.
   A history so organized and documented that the paths of past practice can be easily traced.
Butterfield, Herbert. *The Origins of Modern Science.* London: G. Bell, 1949.
   Critical first steps in modern physics, physiology, astronomy and chemistry described with the suspense of a detective story.
Dampier, Sir William Cecil. *A History of Science and its Relations with Philosophy and Religion.* Cambridge: University Press, 1949.
   Combines wide historical scholarship with profound knowledge of modern physics and a comprehensive outlook on modern biology.
Conant, James B. *Modern Science and Modern Man.* New York: Columbia University Press, 1953.
   A description of the philosophical implications of modern physics and chemistry.
Conant, James B. *On Understanding Science; an Historical Approach.* New Haven: Yale University Press, 1947.
   An examination of the problem of how to give the non-scientific scholar a better understanding of pure or basic science.
Finch, James Kip. *Engineering and Western Civilization.* New York: McGraw-Hill, 1951.
   Outlines the history of engineering from the earliest beginnings, some 50 centuries ago, to modern times, noting and commenting upon the accompanying economic and social conditions and their effect upon technological development and progress.
Forbes, Robert James. *Man, the Maker; a History of Technology and Engineering.* New York: Schuman, 1950.
   A compact history of man's technological progress written for the general reader, covering the time-span from the stone age to the era of the jet plane and television.
Jaffe, Bernard. *Men of Science in America.* New York: Simon and Schuster, 1944.
   The role of science in the history of our country as evidenced in the lives of nineteen famous scientists.
Parsons, William B. *Engineers and Engineering in the Renaissance.* Baltimore: Williams and Wilkins, 1939.

Dealing with a neglected and relatively unknown aspect of the Renaissance, this volume calls attention to achievements in building construction, mining technology, the invention of machines, river control, canal building, bridge building, and structural engineering on the continent of Europe.

Sedgwick, William Thompson. *A Short History of Science* (rev. ed.). New York: Macmillan, 1939.

Useful as a brief survey to about the end of the nineteenth century, but twentieth century advances are inadequately treated.

Singer, Charles J. *A Short History of Science*. Oxford: Clarendon Press, 1941.

An elementary survey of the development of the knowledge of the material world which discusses the emergence of leading scientific ideas from Greek times to the nineteenth century.

Taylor, Frank S. *Science, Past and Present*. London: W. Heinemann, 1947. (U.S. edition has title: A Short History of Science and Scientific Thought)

A helpful reference volume for the general reader, with important information from the first use of the lever principle to the splitting of the atom.

SECTION III
Imaginative Literature—Novels, Short Stories

In these the future beneficent, important and possible dominant role of science and engineering may be envisioned, as well as the poetic and aesthetic possibilities of the work of the engineer: The beauty of pattern in science, the majesty and "power" of a great bridge, the artistry of technique in research and design.

Bradbury, Ray. *Fahrenheit 451*. New York: Ballantine Books, 1953.

An alarming picture of our future life, plus two shorter stories by perhaps the most brilliant American writer of science fiction.

Hobart, Alice Tisdale. *Oil for the Lamps of China*. Indianapolis: Bobbs-Merrill, 1933.

The story of a young mining engineer employed by an American Oil company in China and his problems of adjusting to the company and to the culture of the East.

Huxley, Aldous. *Brave New World.* New York: Doubleday, Doran, 1932.
A pessimistic view of conformity and its effect on society.

Lewis, Sinclair. *Arrowsmith.* New York: Harcourt, Brace, 1925.
Martin Arrowsmith lets neither the artificial obstacles of vested complacency nor the real problems of medicine divert him from his urge to find out.

Orwell, George. *Nineteen Eighty Four.* New York: Harcourt, Brace, 1949.
A horrifying portrayal of a society that the author imagined might result if certain tendencies now in evidence were allowed to develop.

SECTION IV
Classics of Modern Science and Engineering

It is thought that great value may be derived from reading the actual works of the great scientists and engineers, that a vital spark of enthusiasm may come from the original fire of creative intelligence directly through their own writing. This is the leading idea of the "Great Books" movement.

Cullimore, Allen R., compiler. *Through Engineering Eyes.* New York: Pitman, 1941.
A collection of the writings of twenty-seven famous men about the development of scientific and engineering thought.

Durand, William F. *Selected Papers.* Pasadena: California Institute of Technology, 1944.
A selection from the writing of "the dean of the engineering profession" which reflects his philosophy of life and approach to the problems of engineering.

Knickerbocker, William S., editor. *Classics of Modern Science.* New York: Crofts, 1940.
A selection of characteristic essays from the writings of famous scientists.

Shapley, Harlow, editor. *A Treasury of Science.* 3rd rev. ed. New York: Harper, 1954.
Useful for acquainting the reader with the best scientific minds of our times through their own words about their own fields.

Smyth, Henry De Wolf. *Atomic Energy for Military Purposes.* Princeton: Princeton University Press, 1945.

The official "Smyth" report of the work leading to the development of the atomic bomb. Gives some concept of the scientific and engineering problems that were overcome.

SECTION V
Education

Books that should be helpful to the student in learning how to study. These show how to use one's intellectual resources efficiently; also what others have thought about the aims of education.

Huxley, Thomas. *Science and Culture.* New York: P. F. Collier, 1910.
Support for the claims of "science" against the "classics" in education.
McGuire, J. G. *An Introduction to the Engineering Profession.* 2nd ed. Cambridge: Addison-Wesley, 1951.
A good guide for the student about to decide on a career in engineering. There are selected readings at the end of each chapter and many appropriate illustrations and photographs.
Newman, John Henry. *The Idea of a University.* New ed. New York: Longmans, 1947.
A critical analysis of the meaning of a liberal education and the purpose of a university.
Osborn, Alex F. *Applied Imagination.* New York: Scribner, 1953.
Principles and procedure of creative thinking. The book's basic message is sound and significant: cultivate the power of imagination in connection with the use of the scientific method and always be kind to other people, encouraging them also to use and develop their creativity.
Robinson, J. H. *Mind in the Making.* New York: Harper, 1921.
A professor of history suggests that the method of thinking employed in the natural sciences should be applied to politics and in the business world.
Russell, Bertrand. *Human Knowledge; its Scope and Limits.* New York: Simon and Schuster, 1948.
"The central purpose of this book is to examine the relation between individual experience and the general body of scientific knowledge."
Swain, G. F. *How to Study.* New York: McGraw-Hill, 1917.
Effective study is a systematic and vigorous attack upon the subject matter. Here's how.

SECTION VI
Social and Political Problems

Books and essays that present the great unsolved social and political problems of the times. In many of these problems the sciences must come to play an important role but, perhaps, have not done so up to now.

Bush, Vannever. *Modern Arms and Free Men.* New York: Simon and Schuster, 1949.
"More than the story of science and war, this book is an interpretation of the impact of science on the relations of men in this changing world."

Lilienthal, David Eli. *TVA; Democracy on the March.* New York: Harper, 1944.
"As one of the administrators from the start and more recently as Chairman of the Tennessee Valley Authority (TVA), Lilienthal writes eloquently of that achievement of democracy and science . . ."

Davis, Kenneth S. *River on the Rampage.* New York: Doubleday, 1953.
The author discusses the tremendous importance of the natural resource, water, and how its management affects both the practice and theory of government and government-business relations, as well as the economic welfare of the people. The river on the rampage is the Kansas River.

Myrdal, Gunnar *et al. American Dilemma; the Negro Problem and Modern Democracy.* New York: Harper, 1944.
"Regardless of whether you are interested in 'the Negro problem' you will find this the most penetrating and important book on our contemporary civilization that has been written."

Whitehead, Alfred N. *Science and the Modern World.* New York: Macmillan, 1925.
"The author analyzes the reactions of science in forming the background of thought of successive generations, studying in particular the influences at work in the seventeenth, eighteenth, and nineteenth centuries."

Wiener, Norbert. *The Human Use of Human Beings, Cybernetics and Society.* New York: Houghton, 1950.
"Cybernetics might be defined as the study of the striking similarities between the human brain and calculating machines. This book

brings the subject up to date and emphasizes social implications as well as technical advances."

SECTION VII
The Industrial World

Allen, Frederick L. *The Big Change: America Transforms Itself, 1900–1950.* New York: Harper, 1952.
> A graphic description of the economic, industrial, and social changes of the first half of this century in America. Other accounts of the same era should be read in conjunction with this one.

Childs, Marquis and Douglass Cater. *Ethics in a Business Society.* New York: Harper, 1954.
> A balanced consideration of the modern problem of the need of ethical behavior, especially by management, in the industrial world of today.

DuPont de Nemours (E. I.) and Co. *DuPont, the Antobiography of an American Enterprise.* New York: Scribner, 1952.

Lilienthal, David Eli. *Big Business, a New Era.* New York: Harper, 1953.
> A well-written and understandable discussion of bigness in business by the former head of the TVA and of the Atomic Energy Commission (AEC).

SECTION VIII
Popular Science

Books on popular science or books written in a scientific vein. These are entertaining and will show that reading about science and engineering can be fun.

Carson, Rachel Louise. *The Sea Around Us.* New York: Oxford University Press, 1951.
> A book that manages to be fascinating yet scientifically accurate in its description of the processes that formed our planet.

Dean, Gordon. *Report on the Atom; What You Should Know About the Atomic Energy Program of the United States.* New York: Knopf, 1953.
> A history of the first ten years of the Atomic Age, of the development

of atomic energy, not only in the U.S., but elsewhere in the world, including an obviously and necessarily restrained estimate of the Russian advances.

Dugan, James. *The Great Iron Ship.* New York: Harper, 1953.

The almost incredible story of the Great Eastern, launched in 1858, larger than any vessel built until the turn of the century. Although she laid the first Atlantic cable, her lack of success was so marked that she was auctioned six times and ended as an advertising stunt moored in the Mersey.

Heyerdahl, Thor. *The Kon-Tiki Expedition; by Raft Across the South Seas.* London: Allen and Unwin, 1950.

Tells the story of how the author and five others traveled from Peru to a small island east of Tahiti in a balsa raft built as men of the stone age could have built it.

Hogben, Lancelot Thomas. *Mathematics for the Million.* New York: Norton, 1940.

The fact that this volume, with numerous graphs and equations—as well as charming sketches—replete with difficult problems, became a best seller, is proof enough of its originality, its vitality, its exciting appeal.

Ley, Willy. *Engineer's Dreams.* New York: Viking Press, 1954.

A series of highly readable descriptions of promising but unexecuted projects in which all Ley's talents as an entertaining, factual expositor of science come to the fore.

Marek, Kurt W. *Gods, Graves and Scholars,* by C. W. Ceram (pseud). New York: Knopf, 1951.

A popular story of the great archaeological discoveries of the last two centuries, and of the men who made them in Pompeii, Troy; Crete, Egypt, Assyria, Babylonia, Sumeria, and Yucatan. The best popular history of archaeology, written with zest and packed with information.

Moore, Ruth E. *Man, Time, and Fossils; the Story of Evolution.* New York: Knopf, 1953.

A lucid and engrossing account of the story of evolution, handsomely illustrated with photographs and a wealth of line drawings.

Miller, Henry W. *The Paris Gun; the Bombardment of Paris by the German Long Range Guns and the Great German Offensives of 1918.* New York: Cape and H. Smith, 1930.

The excitement, the horror, and the devastation in Paris, the tension and tragedy at the guns—all find a place in this narrative of great power and lucidity.

Answers to Selected Problems

2.1 Critical path = 16 weeks.

3.2 Text points out that maximum indecision is one-half unit in last significant place.

	READING	INDECISION	MAX. VALUE	MIN. VALUE
Jordans	420	.5	420.5	419.5
Cleaners	1100	50	1150	1050
Wire pit	4735	5	4740	4730
	INPUT		6310.5 max.	6199.5 min.

Output reading = 6250 gpm $\therefore$ indecision = 5 gpm

Max. input − min. output = 6310.5 − 6245 = 66 gpm
(leakage *out*)

Min. input − max. output = 6199.5 − 6255 = −56 gpm
(leakage *in*)

Note: We could round-off wire pit reading before calculations but this would be less accurate, it would seem.

3.3 Absolute error = naA^{n-1}

3.7 $x = 0.68, y = 1.46.$

3.8 $R_f = 20$ ohms, $V_t \approx 113$ volts
$R_f = 33.3$ ohms, $V_t = 100$ volts
$R_f = 50$ ohms, $V_t = 50$ volts
20 percent speed reduction
$R_f = 20$ ohms, $V_t = 87$ volts
$R_f = 33.3$ ohms, $V_t = 60$ volts
$R_f = 50$ ohms, $V_t = 20$ volts

3.11 156 mph

4.1 0.307

4.2 0.4375

4.3 0.039

4.4 0.28

4.7 0.63

4.9 (a) 0.031
(c) 0.965

5.1 Assuming the digger must be rented for a full day, hand labor should be used unless there are more than 26 sections to be installed.

5.2 14 floors

6.1 765 ft lb

6.2 5090 joules

6.3 1.8×10^5 ft lb

6.4 25.8 ft

7.1 Work $= -5760$ ft lb done on piston by gas. Weight of piston is constant thus pressure is constant.

7.2 79.4 Btu added to gas. Use first law.

7.3 $T_f = 750°R$ and $p_f = 30$ psia

7.4 (a) $T_f = 1500°R$
(b) $Q = 27.4$ Btu

7.5 Carnot engine efficiency is 26.8%. Don't believe the inventor. Suggest he take a basic course in thermodynamics.

7.7 Carnot requires a refrigeration efficiency of 12.5. Actual efficiency is 19.

8.3 $B = 0.8 \times 10^6$ Hz. Not satisfactory for TV.

8.5 (a) $C = 10 \times 10^6$ bits/s
(b) double bandwidth

8.7 (a) 16 levels
(b) 16 levels requires 4 pulses
(c) PAM requires 16 μs and PCM requires 64 μs

Index